# INTEGRAL TRAIN
# SYSTEMS

# INTEGRAL TRAIN SYSTEMS

## BY JOHN G. KNEILING, M.E., P.E., CONSULTING ENGINEER

A KALMBACH  PUBLICATION

Library of Congress Catalog Card Number:
75-76387

# PREFACE

This book is the first to deal with integral train technology and hence it assumes no body of literature with which readers could be familiar. It therefore necessarily includes material covering a wide range of topics — from quite elementary to fairly sophisticated.

No single book can make an expert, and in a relatively new field the ongoing changes demand resourcefulness, an inquiring turn of mind, and some iconoclasm. The present book presents the basics and some illustrations that can help managers, engineers, regulators, and traffic men to use the new technology and the services of men skilled in its application. For some years to come it can safely be assumed that there will be a value in the experience that any practitioner can gain by working in this field and participating in new-systems research — the technology is far from ready for a "handbook" that can substitute for thought.

This book assumes some familiarity with transportation, particularly rail transportation; but it does not assume that its readers will be specialists or experts in rail transportation. Railroad men, particularly, will find much to "unlearn" because there are many departures from past practices.

When nontechnical matters are considered in this book, no particular political or economic "philosophy" is advocated. The treatment and its intent are entirely pragmatic and are intended to help to cope with conditions as they are and appear likely to be — all in a commercial context.

This book is divided into four parts:

1 — Concepts
2 — Technology
3 — Money
4 — Commercial Exploitation

It is intended that most users will read at least the leading paragraphs throughout the book and for this purpose they are set in contrasting type. Such a "skimming" process will yield a brief, though superficial, review of the subject. All readers — including those interested in specialties — are advised to do so in order to help understand the relationship between each area of special interest and other phases of integral train system origin and application.

Most readers below top-management levels will be concerned with individual sections. Each will find that integral train technology is an extension or application of principles with which he has long been familiar — there are few wholly new or "far out" developments. The central consideration is that the new technology is a reasonable derivative of the consistent application of accepted — though often ignored — basic concepts.

The two appendices concern:

a — Some projections that will help anticipate next-generation equipment. All the components are now available and next-generation equipment could be had quickly once an adequately motivated project started to seek it.

b — A glossary of terms which have special definitions in integral train technology. All readers are advised to study this glossary — most application problems will arise, at least in part, from failure to agree on definitions. As is usual in technology, the definitions are precise.

This book has no index. It is organized to be its own index. The subdivisions are small enough that a reader seeking a specific reference can find a suitably descriptive subtitle and then read the subsection involved.

Since this is the first published book on this subject, it must be directed to various needs — including those of top-level managers, operating men, sales and traffic men, equipment designers, consultants, and others. It is therefore not surprising that it represents some compromise with diverse needs and it cannot be entirely specialized to any one set of requirements.

It is necessary to caution against undertaking treatment of complex problems and complex system planning without adequate help — as was noted above, no single book can make an expert. Persons undertaking serious planning must be of analytical or inquiring turns of mind, or have the aid of such persons. However, managers and others only incidentally interested in transportation can find much that they can use in this book — not the least of which is the design "philosophy" used, which is also useful in other technological areas. Manager-generalists using technological help will find it useful to evaluate such specialized assistance in terms of planning flexibility and analytical treatment displayed.

# SUMMARY

Integral train technology starts with some almost painfully obvious but ordinarily neglected concepts. They amount to a strictly commercial plan to run each train as if it were intended solely to produce low-cost — low **total** cost — transportation.

The train needs accessories to load and unload, service, fuel, and maintain it. These accessories are essential to the economic operation of the train. The entire system is an integral train **system.**

It also follows that an integral train system will use and pay **directly** for only those railroad plant and facility components that it needs — it is not run to move cars or make up trains. It runs to deliver — not just carry — freight. It will also contribute to "overhead and profit," and this money can be used in any way that management chooses.

Engineering decisions derive from commercial ideas. For performing any function there are many tools and methods. Engineering design consists of selecting, for each function, the tool and method associated with lowest total cost. It does make a difference how the work is done.

A first commercial choice is usually a single-purpose facility or device. Traditionalists will ask why multipurpose systems are seldom used, especially since so many of them already exist. The correct reply is: "Your existing facility would be used if it could compete in cost with the recommended single-purpose facility."

It will startle some to learn that few existing transportation systems and accessories survive such analysis. The shocks are often salutary.

Engineering design, then, is a series of choices, each directed to reducing total out-of-pocket costs (by definition: incremental — do not use the **ICC definition) of the operation being planned.** Neighboring operations usually are neither improved nor disadvantaged by using integral train systems. The consultant says, "We'll worry about them when they become clients."

This rationale tacitly concedes that each bit of business must meet at least its own incremental costs and rejects the concept of cross-subsidy except insofar as the "contribution to overhead and profit" is used to subsidize "deserving" operations.

Engineering design is separated from equipment sales in cost-oriented design so that low-capital alternatives can be seriously evaluated. Lowest **total** cost is usually associated with limited-scope, low-budget systems planned for fast amortization — usually to the commercial annoyance of machinery vendors.

This concept of limited objectives will also disturb traditionally acculturated engineers, few of whom think commercially. This is not to propose compromising adequacy. It takes rare sophistication to avoid waste and still get a job done — adequately — once.

Budgeting is an important part of the planning process because costs enter into all design decisions and commercial considerations. The common practice of budgeting separately after "design" is "finished" adversly affects the search for lowest **total** cost because design decisions tend to be made independently of costs.

It is necessary, first, to appreciate the objectives of the budgeting process and hence the applicability — or inapplicability — of traditional costing processes. Many implementation-stage problems will arise because critics apply traditional "cost" rationale where it was not intended and does not apply.

Integral train systems have the incidental but useful characteristic of enabling most of their costs to be isolated and hence indentified. It is also characteristic of integral train systems that their management can be largely isolated from the management of the rest of the railroad. Therefore advances in technology and operational science need not wait for the rest of the industry. The savings from such advances can be realized and identified at once. Obviously these conditions will please some and distress others — and can be used to inhibit or respond to the less rational of critics. Theory or no, this is an area of concern to innovators.

This same capacity for isolation and consequent emphasis on superficial novelty can help to avoid some of the most irrational regulatory problems without compromising the intent of the law or demanding that regulators (or others) publicly admit past errors.

# CONTENTS

# 1. CONCEPTS

There is nothing arcane about concepts of technology. The totality
of concepts can be expressed thus:

> Plan and run the train and any accessories it needs as if they
> existed solely to produce the needed hauling and handling at
> minimum total cost. Treat all dollars as if they were equally
> important and let policy men divide the job — and the profits
> after there is something to divide. Stick to an economic — i.e.,
> commercial — orientation and avoid intellectual or commercial
> conflicts of interest. And do not yield at all to "compromise"
> proposals based on nothing more meritorious than intellectual
> rigidity.

The first necessary concept is that of a train and accessories as a
self-contained tool with quite specific application. It is not a group of
generalized (and hence compromised) cars whose random movements
and supervision deny the existence of a system or coherent objective.
The rationale is that of a ship — with hinges to get around the curves,
but a ship nevertheless. Its normal state is in motion; traditional railroading conceives of cars as normally standing still.

Its management must nearly always be separated from traditional
railroad management — a concession to existing widespread managerial rigidity and the frustrating array of unrelated problems involved
in railroading when treated generally. It is simply not practical in commercially available time to effect real improvements in railroad managerial philosophy without evaluating reasons for this condition. It is
practical to detour around most of the problems and obsolete ideas —
and use the lines whose managers **can** and **will** progress, or at least
allow progress to occur. It usually follows that the services integral
train systems buy from railroad managements are minimized. This is
opposite to the idea — popular among traditional traffic men — of placing maximum "responsibility" on the railroad. (Too many traffic men
use this catch-phrase to seek something for nothing and it never
works.)

Typically a railroad will be invited (or will propose) to supply a
driver, such "helpers" (assumed nonworkers) as its union can effectively demand, use of its track, supervision of its help and liability for its
own negligence. Integral train system budgets isolate and identify these
costs. Typically a railroad will not be invited to make any investments
in a shipper-conceived system. It will be offered the opportunity to
supply a defined service, at a profit, on no investment (with a bonus-

penalty clause for speed). The only direct measure of railroad performance typically is celerity in getting the train over the road, once the system is designed and in use.

Integral train planners must, within their own organizations, resolve such matters as real concern with costs, managerial willingness to concern themselves with the "nuts and bolts" of carriage, etc. Resistances like "we just don't want to" or "we are not in that business" must be resolved early. The only shipper incentive in most cases is money. Many businesses have other and more pressing or highly regarded objectives.

Integral train systems can be applied to a wide variety of uses. They need not be shuttles — shuttles represent only a few and not even the commercially most promising applications. The planner must keep before him the concept of a ship sailing on an iron ocean — not a fleet of randomly moving, individual, multipurpose cars.

Capital costs must be converted into annual costs and be included in an expense budget before counting profit. Internally generated or not, capital must be treated as if it were borrowed at an applicable interest rate. The question of "whose capital?" must be deferred until after the system is planned.

All choices must be pragmatic, objective and commercial.

> *For example:* Some routes have adverse labor conditions. It is seldom practical to seek improvement — the train either "pays the toll" or goes elsewhere — all or nothing.

Some technological and conceptual intermediates are useful compromises, but most are mere "gimmicks" to prevent change, devised by someone who feels insecure. A system planner must develop a talent for identifying and coping with these situations despite a cultural tendency among engineers to hold such "political" and personality considerations in low repute.

A system planner, likely to be the "free-lancer" type, must often convince an "organization man" type. Resulting conflicts must be resolved by concurrence, truce, economic necessity, or fiat; but they must be resolved. The common meeting ground must usually be an objective commercial attitude. The planner must be prepared to reply to many critics essentially thus:

> *Question:* "Do we have to do it that way?" — or variation.
> *Reply:* "No, but it will cost more or earn less if you do not."
> And he must prove the point; hence the elaborate budgeting — integral train technology makes cost differentials difficult to conceal. There is little room for "Cost is what someone says it is."

When this reply proves inadequate, the planned is well advised to direct his effort to objectives that his employer **does** value.

## 1.1 Basic Premises

Integral train technology is logically derived by consistently applying basic premises. Taken together they make up a body of concepts which must be comprehended in toto. Separately they mean little. It is unproductive to study application details without this basic understanding.

There are three basic premises (and some accessories):

A — The "system" concept states that any commercially significant set of related operations makes up a system whose components, separately, are not significant.

B — The commercial logistics concept states that transportation is part of a logistics system that includes functions traditionally found in other jurisdictions and that a rational treatment must consider this logistics system as an entity.

C — The incremental cost concept refers to all costs incurred to carry out a function which would not be incurred if the function were not carried out. It has two applications and has no substitute in either.

### 1.1.1. The "System" Concept

An integral train has no importance *by itself*. The planning unit is an integral train system comprising — by definition — the train, its spare parts, "shop" units, and accessories. The accessories include (at least) loading, unloading, and train service facilities. System unity is vital despite the fact that the parts may be found in (at least) shipper, railroad and consignee jurisdictions.

Loading and unloading facilities are vital (though not traditionally included in transportation) primarily because they affect the all-important utilization of the costly train. For example:

Hypothecate a volume of 1,500,000 tons per year.

Case "A," cycle time 88 hours; 100 cycles per year.

Train size, 15,000 tons (1/100 of 1,500,000).

Train investment, $7,500,000 @ $500 per capacity ton.

Case "B," cycle time 84 hours (reduce terminal and/or travel time by 4 hours); 103 cycles per year.

Train size, 14,100 tons (1/103 of 1,500,000).

Train investment, $7,100,000 @ $500 per capacity ton.

Station: (no change in travel time)

Case "A": discharge 15,000 tons in 8 hr. @ 2,000 tph.

Case "B": discharge 14,100 tons in 4 hr. @ 3,500 tph.

Difference in station capital:

| | |
|---|---|
| Wider belt: $10 × 600 feet (belt extends to top of 200-foot surge pile) | $ 6,000 |
| 300 additional horsepower @ $100 | 30,000 |
| Total | 36,000 |

| | |
|---|---|
| Gross saving (train investment) | 400,000 |
| Additional station cost | — 36,000 |
| Net capital saving | $364,000 |

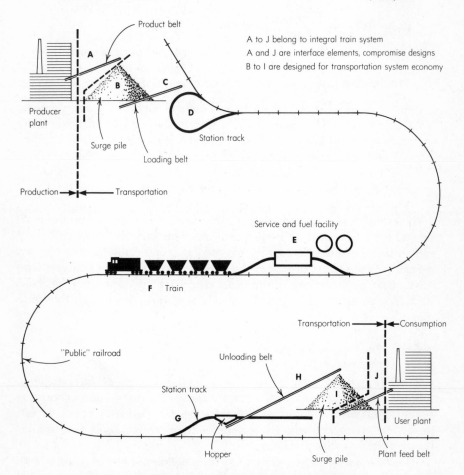

A to J belong to integral train system
A and J are interface elements, compromise designs
B to I are designed for transportation system economy

**1.1.1 — Principal Components of an Integral Train System**

The system, for design purposes, must encompass all the elements that are vital to its economy, regardless of traditional divisions of responsibility. The interface elements make the transition from patron to transportation needs, and all else — including the surge piles or their equivalents — is designed for total transportation economy. The system usually contains its own train service facility but its train runs on the "public" railroad.

The capital saving of $400,000 in train equipment can be had by spending $36,000 for a wider and faster belt. In most economically designed integral train bulk terminals the only element that differs materially with station speed capability is the belt that directly serves the train. Capital usually dominates such comparisons, since capital charges account for about as much as all other elements combined.

An alternative computation in this case can use a total train time value of $200 per hour. The **station** will use train time thus:

Case "A"   $\dfrac{1,500,000}{2,000} \times \$200 = \$150,000$ per year.

Case "B"   $\dfrac{1,500,000}{3,500} \times \$200^* = \underline{\quad 86,000 \quad}$

Saving   $64,000 per year on $36,000 investment.

*The smaller train has a lower value, so the saving is slightly understated.

Similar considerations apply to mechanical facilities, long turnouts, train phones, etc. The very real cost savings can be had only when the system is designed as a unit. Traditional economy studies "reason" thus:

Let traffic men negotiate the longest "free" time they can and then train time costs nothing. At 8 hours "free" time the $36,000 is "consignee's money" and cannot be compared with $400,000 of "railroad's money."

As one of many bits of icing on the cake, the faster station can be served by a one-shift railroad yard crew (in yard limits), while any conventional plant will usually use two railroad crew days — plus an industry crew to pass cars over the hopper. Economists or analysts who assert that plant dollars differ from equipment dollars must be dealt with on a policy level — most banks claim that dollars are all the same size.

### 1.1.2 The Logistics Concept

**Total functional cost is the commercial criterion of effectiveness. Shipping room, transportation, warehouse, inventory and receiving room are all parts of logistics — despite the fact that they normally fall to diverse managers, usually jealous of their prerogatives and prematurely occupied with divisions.**

*For example:* **The concept has been colloquialized in these words: "A buck is a buck — design the whole bit as if one outfit owned it all and *then* figure out how to divide it up."**

The system concept says that everything that affects utilization and performance must be part of a system. The same rationale applies to accessories. The literature calls the idea logistics or physical distribution, but the central theme is that transportation does not exist in a vacuum. Traditionally, shipping rooms, warehouses — everything within factory walls — belonged to "production." Transportation was gate-to-gate.

A planning unit must reach all accessories — even across traditional lines. A planner can spend all he likes, anywhere, if he saves $1.01, somewhere, for every $1.00 he spends. The scope of even the feasibility study is from within a producer's plant to within a user's plant. The planner must sometimes mediate between managements — both jealous of their prerogatives.

Old-line production men saw material and finished goods inventories as existing to protect their schedules and not subject to value analysis, which they did not trust anyway. Actually they belong to transportation — and are subject to economic analysis like all other parts of the logistics system.

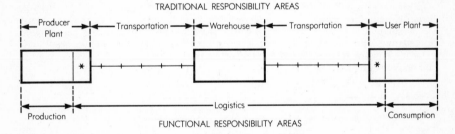

TRADITIONAL RESPONSIBILITY AREAS

Producer Plant — Transportation — Warehouse — Transportation — User Plant

Production — Logistics — Consumption

FUNCTIONAL RESPONSIBILITY AREAS

*Shipping, packaging, receiving, storage, etc , within plant walls

#### 1.1.2 — The Logistics Concept

The concept of industrial logistics says that all available alternates must be within one system so that economic choices can be made on economic bases. It says that "all dollars are equally important" and that artificial boundaries should not exclude, arbitrarily, any economic alternates. This concept merely expresses a real concern with economy. It will meet with some resistance from those with vested interests in existing *divisions* of responsibilities.

### 1.1.3   The Incremental Cost Concept

**Incremental cost is defined as all costs, by whomever incurred, which are incurred if a task is performed and are not incurred if it is not performed. All other costs are "overhead." Any sale that will not pay at least its incremental costs is not wanted — in any trade. Excess of income over incremental cost is applied first to fixed costs and then to profit. If an enterprise does not have enough aggregate excess of income over incremental costs, its salvation does not lie in turning away any contributions to the fund from which "overhead" and then profit are drawn.**

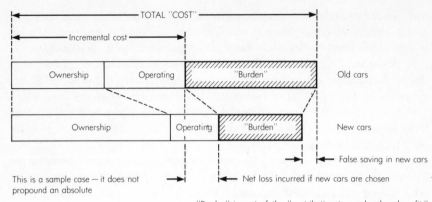

This is a sample case — it does not propound an absolute

"Burden" is part of the "contribution to overhead and profit," regardless of nomenclature, and seldom avoids distortion — "burden" often is assigned by number of cars; and new, larger cars are assigned less burden, but the assignment is artificial

### 1.1.3-A — "Costs" for Decision-Making

Regardless of other criteria, choices intended to yield the best economy must be based on incremental costs. All "burden" schemes exist merely for accounting convenience in assigning shared costs. For example, using burdened costs to select cars would adversely affect the bottom line of the P&L statement, regardless of how costs, savings and profits are eventually divided or assigned.

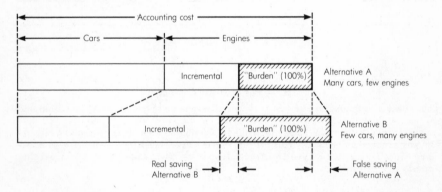

"Burden" properly belongs in "contribution to overhead and profit" and is irrelevant to this choice. Distortions are inevitable when comparing dissimilar alternatives and using burdened rates

### 1.1.3-B — Distortions Arising from "Burdened" Costs

In this example a choice involving two kinds of equipment, burdened differently, is made avoidably obscure when burdened costs are used. The only way to compare dissimilar things in a business context is by their effect on the balance sheet. This is not to criticize the use of burdened costs to perform accounting functions. It is to suggest that when making decisions based on costs, only those costs that eventually affect the balance sheet differentially with respect to the choice at hand are pertinent. If the accountants call two items dissimilar, or so treat them, care must be taken. (Most "standard" cost systems name this weakness but better semantics.)

A useful illustration of this concept can be found in attempts to 'justi-fy" new 100-ton cars when existing 70-ton cars would be more econom-ic. The "cost" of the cars consists of:

A — Ownership cost, a function of investment.

B — Operating cost, mostly maintenance.

C — Allocated cost, which on many railroads includes items allocated on the basis of number of cars.

In the illustration:

A — Operating cost is smaller for the new cars but is small in both cases.

B — Ownership cost is higher for the new cars — they must be bought at current prices.

Analysis directed to the net effect on the balance sheet (incremental cost analysis by definition) will recommend the older cars. Yet rail-roads have allowed lower rates on big (new) cars. In effect they say:

"We like big cars and if you buy them we will put up some of the money in the form of reduced contributions to our over-head and profit."

If the planner's client is a shipper, he tends to accept.

The other sketch illustrates another error. A total cost involves cash outlays and a "burden" — here based on engine-hours. To reduce "total cost" the number of engine-hours can be reduced, producing a longer cycle and needing more cars. The fallacy arises because engine-hours are made to look expensive by the allocated burden. The result is anti-economic to the user (but not to a carbuilder).

Similar observations apply to many types of system costs — e.g., the initial track maintenance, which is seldom even identified in railroad ac-counts. Similarly, "high-horsepower engines" are sometimes "justified" because railroad accounting apportions certain elements of engine maintenance cost to "car bodies." Two engines on one frame can thus be sold, with every accessory duplicated, higher than the two would sell for separately — reversing usual expectations.

Planners' concern is with the net effect on a consolidated balance sheet. Such a single-minded concern will provide the most useful guideline to choices. Caution is needed to insure that all incremental costs are included, wherever found, and that no costs are included that do not actually vary with the decision being made.

Planners should note that the definition of incremental cost is not related to "direct" or "out of pocket" costs as defined for other uses. It should also be noted that incremental costs may vary among enter-prises for the same task. The pertinent variable is the array of avail-able choices.

### 1.1.4   Tare Weight Economics

A tare weight economy calculation can illustrate a commercial relationship. The cost of hauling the gross load is incurred when the train
is run. If tare can be replaced by payload, the *incremental* effect on
the balance sheet is measured by applying the *freight rate* — not any
actual or imputed cost or profit — to the number of ton-miles involved.

To illustrate: Consider a car that runs 250 miles per day (about 10
mph), 300 days per year, 50% empty, where the freight rate is 3.0 mills
per ton-mile. Its gross is 263,000 pounds and tare can be either 50,000
pounds or 60,000 pounds. How much more is the lighter car *worth* than
the heavier car? Or how much less than the lighter car must the heavier
car be priced to be economically equivalent?

Annual loaded mileage:  $\dfrac{250 \times 300}{2} = 37,500$

Differential tare: 10,000 pounds or 5 tons
Annual improved productivity of the lighter car is:
  $5 \times 37,500 = 187,500$ ton-miles
Additional annual revenue is:
  $0.003 \times 187,500 = \$562.50$

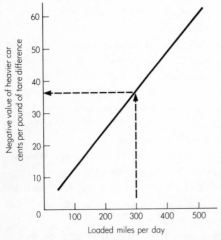

Cents-per-pound capital value for
**eliminating** tare for:
  • Freight rate 1 mill/ton-mile
  • Interest and amortization 15%
    (10 years, 8%, no salvage)
**not** including cost of excess tare in light
movements

**Example:**

A car loaded 300 miles per day, at 5 mills per ton-mile,
weighing 54,000 pounds, is **worth**
  $\$0.36 \times 6,000 \times 5 = \$10,800$
more than a car weighing 60,000 pounds, regardless of
the **price** of either

*(chart axes: "Negative value of heavier car cents per pound of tare difference" at 0, 10, 20, 30, 40, 50, 60; "Loaded miles per day" at 100, 200, 300, 400, 500)*

#### 1.1.4 — Tare Weight Economy

In the case illustrated, if the lighter car can be bought for $10,800, then the heavier
car has *no* value — in terms of ability to earn money — regardless of its cost. At attainable utilizations for integral train operations the negative value of excess tare can be
large. For example, the negative value of a 20-lb. nonessential item like a badge plate
can be $20 or more — even if it costs nothing.

Interest and amortization rate used in this example: 14%
(about 10-year amortization, no salvage, 8% interest)

Annual income of $562.50 will support an investment of:

$$\frac{562.50}{0.14} = \$4,017 \text{ or 40 cents per pound of tare reduction.}$$

This value will be higher if (a) the car has a salvage value to reduce the interest and amortization factor, (b) utilization is higher, (c) the freight rate is higher, or (d) the cost of hauling the heavier car, empty, for 37,500 miles per year is considered.

For example, if it costs an incremental 0.8 mills per ton-mile to haul tare, then the reduction in cost of hauling tare will be $0.0008 \times 187,500 = \$150.00$ per year, which will support

$$\frac{\$150}{.14} = \$1,071 \text{ in additional capital.}$$

The **value** of the lighter car is thus:

$$\begin{array}{r} \$4,017 \\ \text{plus} \quad \underline{1,071} \\ \$5,088 \end{array} \quad \text{more than the value of the}$$

heavier car, regardless of their prices.

In conventional railroading where the empty is part of a random consist, the lighter empty may permit more payload elsewhere in the train. In such a case the gross freight rate is applicable even when the car runs empty.

To illustrate the influence of utilization, the computation for the same car in conventional service (9,000 loaded and 9,000 empty miles per year) at a freight rate of 6 mills per ton-mile is:

Improved productivity: $\dfrac{10,000}{2,000} \times 9,000 = 45,000$ ton-miles.

Additional revenue is $0.006 \times 45,000 = \$270.00$.

Cost difference to handle the car empty at 0.8 mills per ton-mile is $0.0008 \times 45,000 = \$36.00$ per year.

Total annual difference is $270.

$$\begin{array}{r} \underline{36} \\ \$306 \end{array}$$

At the same amortization rate this saving is worth only $2,186 capital, even though the freight rate is twice that used in the first case.

The high utilizations of integral trains *motivate* low-tare designs. The sheltered lives of integral train cars *permit* low-tare designs by limiting structural and mechanical demands on the cars.

### 1.1.5  Time Value Concept

All industrial tools exist to make money, and they all represent capital — even if it is only their unrealized junk value. Therefore all tools have a time value — imputed rental — often called ownership cost — mostly rental on money but including all time costs. This cost runs continuously. There is no free time. "Book value" has nothing to do with the matter.

> *For example:* If time values are stated in days, cost figures will show no incentive to improve utilization unless entire days can be saved. Most attainable improvements are *individually* small (but large in total) and would thereby be lost.

There is *no* free time. If some days cannot be sold (like a saloon in a blue-law state), the unit cost of "sold" or "sellable" time must be increased. The only way to make it hard for anyone to "beat the system" is to charge for *all* days — and charge whoever uses them.

> *For example*: If a car gets 20 trips a year and is allowed 4 "free" days per trip, it will have
> $$365 - (4 \times 20) = 285 \text{ days to sell.}$$
> If it costs $1,000 per year, each "sellable" day costs
> $$\frac{1,000}{285} = \$3.41.$$
> But if all days are charged, each is worth
> $$\frac{1,000}{365} = \$2.69$$
> and shippers will be motivated — at least a little — to use fewer days.

Time spent doing anything — or nothing — costs money because the car represents money and a banker counts all the days. A function may or may not be productive — or avoidable. It still costs money to own a piece of machinery. And it is seldom advisable to conceal, distort or combine costs.

### 1.1.6  Profit vs. Capital Recovery

Time cost must be paid *before* counting profits or alternatives involving differing amounts of capital are not comparable. When capital cost is so charged, such questions as "Whose capital?" or "How much must be invested to obtain the cost saving?" do not arise.

What is sometimes called cash flow is also sometimes misleadingly called return on investment or profit. The first piece of cash flow, here called I&A (for interest and amortization) is what the money would have brought if loaned. The second, here called T&I (for taxes and in-

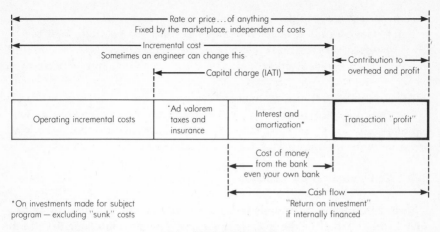

**1.1.6 — What Is "Profit"?**

This diagram illustrates the relationship among several common components of what is loosely called "profit." Planners should use these terms cautiously because, to many men in management positions, they are emotionally "loaded" — with sometimes unexpected meanings.

surance) is money paid out as a consequence of owning an asset. The rest is entrepreneurial profit. To illustrate:

An asset cost $100,000 and has a prospective salvage value of $30,000 at the end of 10 years, during which time it is deemed advisable to plan to close the commitment. It can produce $25,000 per year "operational profit." Money can be loaned at 6%. The correct analysis is:

Interest and amortization on $70,000
    (level annual rate)     $9,800 per year.
Interest on $30,000       1,800
     Total I&A    11,600 .
Taxes and insurance, at a level rate
 of 6% of initial value     6,000
     Total IATI    17,600

This leaves $25,000 — $17,600 = $7,400 "profit." Most traditional economy studies would report either $25,000 or $19,000 ($25,000 — $6,000 T&I) — and then disagree over whose $100,000 should be invested to "earn" 19% or 25%.

## 1.2 Peripheral Concepts

**Some peripheral concepts encountered in integral train systems are what an engineer would call "legitimate" compromises and some are mere "gimmicks."**

There are three groups:

    A — Conceptual intermediates — e.g., unit trains and super-
      — vised services.

    B — Technological intermediates — e.g., blocked and captive
      cars.

    C — Conceptual and managerial isolation.

The first two are fairly obvious, but the third may encounter acceptance problems. Integral train system planners thus must review
the subject in the light of applicable organizational situations.

### 1.2.1 Conceptual Intermediates

**Most conceptual intermediates are offered in an attempt to mini-
mize change. Most of them are economically and technologically (and
intellectually) lacking and should be adopted only when noneconomic
or antieconomic conditions compel.**

A few examples will illustrate this phenomenon. They are chosen
from recent actions by railroads under pressure to develop some, at
least apparent, cost savings.

*The "gathering" bit.* One railroad published a tariff that
allowed "unit train" coal shippers to assemble cars from several mines. It allowed shippers to load cars at any mine in a
designated territory, billed for a specific train and to load those
cars along with other cars. In theory a "unit train's" cars
would move to the assembly point in the "mine runs" and there
be assembled for the trip to the consuming plant.

In fact this was only a volume discount. There was no practical plan to improve mine-run schedule reliability — the original source of much of the cost. Inevitably the system got random cars and no longer could use average weights. Inevitably
mines were allowed to "fill out" from no-bill banks when mine-
run schedules were irregular. The eventual effect was merely
to bunch the cars, increase yard costs at the assembly point,
and further delay mine runs by requiring that "unit train" cars
be switched out.

*Nonspecialized cars.* Another railroad used a "controlled
service" scheme. In theory a certain class of identical cars
would be assigned to the new service, marked with a symbol
and subject to tightened free-time rules. These cars then would
be placed, empty, by the mine runs against orders for cars to be
loaded for this service. The mines would load them in the usual
manner but would be required to bill them to the assigned
schedule.

The cars were subject to the usual car service rules — they were only "special" to the extent of the painted symbol, so connections used them like any other coal cars. The marked cars were "buried" and mine-run schedules became even more unreliable when they had to be switched out.

In due course other cars had to be substituted as the marked cars dispersed under car service rules (as used, not necessarily as written), and "shortages" developed. Random cars forced resumption of weighing and switching by number — brakemen could no longer identify the cars any other way.

*Poor scheduling control.* A railroad using standard cars with a symbol found that long mining region turnarounds derived from mine-run handling. With poor sales communication to complicate matters the assembly points were assembling a "unit train" before the previous one left. No longer could *all* marked cars go into the current unit train and the yards were back to switching by number but with new constraints on departure schedules.

These examples will make the central point clear. It is not practical to maintain a reliable control when the cars are handled conventional-

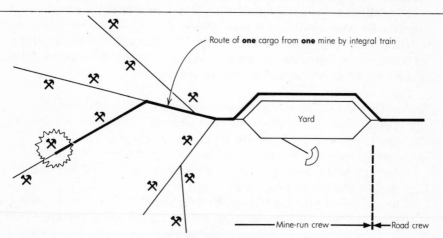

Route of **one** cargo from **one** mine by integral train

Yard

Mine-run crew ►◄ Road crew

#### 1.2.1 — One Mine at a Time

Typically a group of local trains — called "mine runs" in the coalfields — take random empties from the yard to several mines and return with loads. In many "unit train" plans these cars are merely assembled or "bunched" at the yard for road movement — after paying the high cost of the yard and the fleet of locals. In an economically planned integral train operation the empty train inbound and the loaded train outbound bypass the yard directly to and from the mine that is to be served on that particular trip. Once the train is yarded and/or its cars are mixed with others, a large package of avoidable costs is incurred. A mine-run crew will run the train in mine-run territory to avoid labor problems.

ly or as part of an overall operation. In coal the weakest point is the mine run, but if that "hole" is plugged, others will appear in all makeshift operations. All that is accomplished in most such cases is a waste of time — which procrastinators will define as victory ("Do it after I retire").

Most such proposals are motivated by a desire to avoid change, per se. (In all these examples the integral train should go directly to the mine, if necessary visiting several mines to be part-loaded at each, from storage.)

Planners will find two "ground rules" frequently useful:

It is seldom practical to upgrade an existing operation — supervision problems will usually frustrate the attempt even before adequacy problems are encountered.

Planners will usually find certain "signals" in the conferences. When someone wants to use an existing (railroad or shipper) *operation*, a change-minimizing conceptual intermediate is usually being proposed.

### 1.2.2 Technological Intermediates

**Sometimes a "true" integral train is not imediately applicable but some of its central ideas are immediately usable. These ideas usually relate to managerial control over equipment utilization and elimination of nonessential functions (shortening the process as distinguished from improving its parts) and their consequences.**

For example:

To move a limited volume of freight for a considerable distance over two lines, the recommended treatment was to use a block of permanently coupled special cars. At each intermediate yard this block had to move around the hump. At each gateway the train could be yarded and the engine, with the car block attached, could be cut off and run to the enginehouse. There the block could be attached to the departing engine and the assembly then could be coupled to an outbound train, usually hours or days ahead of cars that had to be classified. The mechanical specialization, among other purposes, forced direct handling. Operating forces could not "lose" *these* cars.

This example illustrates isolation from low-echelon management. No one trusted the railroad, at the "grass-roots" level, to take a schedule seriously or to accept the necessity to change past practices unless the change were forced mechanically.

The planner knew that each decision-maker would attach importance to past practice and force the new system to conform — if he could.

In this example, the system was planned for a shipper who proposed to buy the cars provided they were handled in this manner. The railroad was shown the saving that would result and how much of it would be added to railroad profits. However, it responded defensively and offered a mere rate cut — which the shipper accepted.

The economic weakness of most private or captive car plans arises because the cars are handled one at a time and so lose utilization — the usual x-line car problems (though x-line cars, properly supervised, get better utilization than "public" cars). The only practical way to achieve serious utilization improvement is to make it impractical to handle the cars individually.

A further development in this direction is the self-propelled integral car block, which can be used as a head-end unit (*ahead* of the engine).

### 1.2.3 Conceptual and Managerial Isolation

**Most integral train systems seek cost improvements which are, by definition, changes. One planner can make only small inroads on the "way of life" of hundreds of thousands of railroaders. An integral train system must be substantially independent of the rest of the railroad if it is to get off the ground at all — to seek optimum results without awaiting improvements elsewhere. Similarly it is usually less costly — in money and in obstacles — to avoid consequential effects than to budget for them. The idea has been stated:**

> **"Don't try to teach them how to run a railroad — just tell them how to run *this* train."**

This point can be illustrated in several ways.

*Mine runs.* Refer again to the coal operations previously reviewed. Part of the problem was that mine-run operation was so chaotic and unsupervised that no reliable schedule could be maintained. All concerned, typically, presented an imposing array of defenses. But the fact remained that the improvement failed because it tried to adapt to the existing operation and did not isolate itself.

The needed isolation is possible because an integral train has such high capability that very few units are needed and their supervision is thus not burdensome.

*For example:* In a study of Canadian wheat handling it was found that *three* trains, devoting 50% of their time to wheat gathering and hauling, could move 125,000,000 bushels per year directly from the western country elevators to Halifax. These three trains can functionally replace a large array of equipment and facilities and drive a boat system out of business, too. In that case the railroad could not handle that much wheat east of the Lakehead *conventionally* if offered anyway — too much equipment and hence congestion.

The superintendent of a coal-mining division, for example, will find that an integral train will come onto his division once in a while, and when it does, its visit will be an event — just one more event in his life. The mine runs must be scheduled around it until he realizes that it is doing much of their work and he reduces their number.

*For example:* A 40,000 ton integral train on a weekly cycle (not necessarily to the same place every trip) will move 2,000,000 tons per year and will spend only one shift (8 hours) per week in originating territory. Its 1 crew-day per week will account for as much coal as several mine run and yard crews:

40,000 tons = 600 "ordinary" cars, for which:

A) Most mine-run operations will use 20 crew-days, each with overtime, plus four locomotive sets and one spare unit.

B) These same 600 cars a week will also involve two yard shifts per day, 5 days a week, and another engine — at least.

Conventionally run, such an operation will usually consist of:

5 or 6 mine-run crews and some overtime,

2 or more yard crews,

7 to 10 locomotive units,

mechanics, inspectors, etc., plus clerical,

scale, and other peripheral help.

All this can be replaced by one weekly visit of an integral train using one "mine-run" crew which will earn, in most cases, more per man than the superintendent.

To pursue this example, it should be noted that most mining region superintendents are close to mine managements. Their mining friends will welcome the change because there will no longer be any car shortages and few car droppers. The superintendent will find his life greatly easier — once he puts the trauma of change behind him.

## 1.3 Organizational Considerations

An integral train system planner must consider all the realities of his situation — including the nontechnical matters of this section — despite the technical man's tendency to derogate so-called "political" matters. However sound the technology and economics, no *substantive* improvement results if the "personality" situation is hopeless. Technological improvement is often the last resort of business facing disaster after a series of "good guy" decisions. Or it is a tool for invading "fat and happy" trades or of getting defensive rate cuts by exploiting "personalities" who fear technological innovation or are "waiting out a pension."

A planner of technological advance should review three areas:

A — Will business priorities admit his system, profitable or not?

> *For example:* This writer saw a famous manufacturing company block a cost-saving proposal in an executive committee because committeemen "knew" that no profit potential could attract top-management attention unless market penetration were also involved.

B — Resistance to change per se — does anyone want *or need* more profit badly enough to embrace change to get it? Realistically, this decision is personal to each executive.

C — Assorted constraints and anomalies of policy, pride of authorship (toward now-obsolete systems), imminent retirements, nostalgia and the like.

### 1.3.1 Business Objectives and Priorities

Managements are sometimes simply not interested in certain classes of improvements. A management trying to "catch up" in product technology or market penetration just will not even hear of schemes that offer "nothing but money." Treating capital recovery as imputed rental minimizes competition for capital. But it does not remove competition for the attention of top-management talent.

Most integral train systems require part of the time of a talented, knowledgeable senior man — who may have to be imported. An integral train system will rarely require all of his time or effort, but it is usually important enough to assign it a manager of its own. If managing the integral train system is part of a competent man's duties, its essential simplicity can divert his attention to more challenging areas and it will not get the attention it *does* need.

Many businesses do not have enough management talent to assign any to the care of an integral train system — and there is nothing to do but to assign priorities. For example, a business that needs customers badly enough must assign available talent to sales, and cost reduction will just have to wait — though keeping-type money is easier to come by from savings than from new sales.

In the matter of capital, there are many erroneous ideas extant and planners must either correct them or live with them. For example, it is common to finance movable equipment differently from fixed equipment. When such practices are too deeply entrenched, the planner has no choice but to work elsewhere, unless he has such an overwhelming case that it can still "figure."

*For example:* One large company had a choice between $600,000 worth of station gear and $2,500,000 worth of train. Economic planners made a cash-flow analysis, assuming that station gear could not be leased, despite the fact that "lease-back" financing has long been available. They spent the $2,500,000 (via a lease).

A rational treatment would have been to treat both investments alike — all agree that such a lease is effectively equivalent to a mortgage.

### 1.3.2 Resistance to Change

This irrational phenomenon is difficult to treat rationally. Sometimes an important official — he can be at any level — in a profitable, complacent company simply resists change—sometimes admittedly arbitrarily; in effect he is "making enough money."

*For example:* This writer once heard a vice-president say, "This change probably would make us more money. But if I allow one change I must study all the changes offered, and I do not intend to do that. I am not here to make money; I am here to prevent change." A competitor got the order. He's still a v.p.

One theory is that men who elect "organization life" are more likely than "free-lancer" types to display what is sometimes called "natural human resistance to change." The new system planner, usually the free-lancer type, must face this problem — or sell his ideas elsewhere.

Penetrating discussion of this phenomenon properly belongs in a book on psychology or management philosophy. As far as a pragmatic integral train planner is concerned, the condition is simply one of the existing constraints.

The principal task facing an integral train planner is determining whether or not his client (or management) has a way to bypass such an obstacle. If so, he must find it. If not, he must know this fact, because the resistances he will encounter are often so based — regardless of their superficial presentation.

Timely attention can forestall a long and frustrating series of objections, all trivial and unfounded, whereby the planner can *never* propose an acceptable course of action.

### 1.3.3 Constraints and Anomalies

Planners often find senior men personally identified with older systems. The more perceptive know that the old might have merely been the best *then* available. The less perceptive — and less secure —

take proposed changes as personal affronts. This condition is particularly frustrating because such resisters respond defensively and hence irrationally.

*For example:* Many proponents of piggybacking were driven to ask, "What are you trying to perpetuate, the railroad or the boxcar?"

This matter belongs in a psychology book. The integral train planner must avoid wasting his time when this problem exists in aggravated form.

There are several clues; a few will illustrate:

A senior man has presented papers and written — or had ghosted — trade paper articles about a particular facility or system, or even has his name on a plant.

A senior man tends to reminisce excessively.

Senior men seem indispensable — not having trained replacements.

Senior men lecture newcomers at length on "this is how we do things." This habit is not significant at low hierarchical levels.

It would be cheaper to retire such a man — or get him retired. However, when this virus has invaded an organization, top-level policy men are also usually infected, and they keep the yes-men around them. A vendor of new ideas is well advised to visit the competition.

### 1.4 Administration and Operation

An integral train system should be administered as independently as possible of the railroads on which it runs and of the patron plants it serves. (This latter demands suitable interface arrangements.) It can thus achieve improvements without waiting until other operations are improved and can break with the near-fetish of standardization that has burdened the railroad industry. Some design elements are chosen specifically to provide this isolation and permit the train to operate on the rationale of an ocean vessel, not that of a fleet of generalized gear.

The train's normal state should be in motion. When it stops someone should worry until it moves. In contrast a railroader thinks of a car as being normally at rest; its movement is "a project." A railroader asks, "Where can I park it?" The correct reply is, "We planned it so you can't."

It will usually be most economic to supply even fuel and mechanical service at specialized facilities. Proposals to share existing or "common" facilities should be met with a request for quotations — which will usually be higher than costs attainable at new, single-use, budget-design

facilities. The planner must then become obstinate about the priority
of economic objectives. For many programs this issue will be the one
over which the importance that policy men assign to economics will
be resolved.

### 1.4.1 Railroad and Other Labor

**Train crews will normally be employed in accordance with** *existing*
**labor agreements, on railroads and elsewhere. Planners should assume
no improvement in labor practices, featherbedding, quality or supervision. "Nonoperating" labor should be planned as if for a real or
hypothetical service contractor, using nonrailroad labor whenever
possible. Cost figures will often show that it is less costly to use more
labor than more tools and the intangibles favoring less dependence on
labor must then be considered — inflation, reliability, etc.**

Where there is a choice, high-rate, high-quality labor will be less
costly — because of the high value of the equipment. Where no choice
is available — e.g., train crews — equipment must adapt to whatever
help is available. This usually means that train controls must be
essentially automatic in all but their simplest functions.

Especially with nonoperating labor it is usually advisable for any
employee concerned with an integral train to devote all his time to it.

> *For example:* A wayside inspector will be budgeted for a full
> day to perform an inspection that may take only an hour. The
> rationale is that the train will quickly consume more than a
> day's wages in time costs waiting for attention.

The widely publicized on-train featherbedding is wasteful, but it is
a small component of total integral train budgets. An attempt to improve this condition risks a whole program for a small return. Economies in train labor come by eliminating functions — e.g., yards,
gathering trains, etc. — and not seeking marginal savings.

Little should be expected of crewmen. For example, it is usually
inadvisable to expect a brakeman — admittedly idle — to operate the
pushbuttons to open and close car doors. Button-pushing is a separate
job and usually is better automated — for reliability if not for money.

Another place where more labor will be cheaper than more tools is
found where cross-town "yard" crews are used.

> *For example:* A train, by union agreement, may require a
> "yard" crew to move from an arriving line to a departing line.
> The actual transfer takes about 15 minutes. The choices are:
> A — Call a crew and pay a day.
> B — Use a crew already on duty, charging an hour to the
> integral train and risking an average 1-hour delay to
> await the crew's convenience.

A modest-size train will be worth $5 to $7 per minute — upwards of $300 per hour — obviously more than the cost of a crew-day. (The $300 is largely reflected in cycle time and hence equipment.) Thus the choice is between more men and more tools and will favor more men in this case, where the featherbedding cannot be eliminated entirely.

*For example:* In a sophisticated system the economic choice between manual and automatic door pushbuttons is usually marginal. However, the system is usually sensitive to unreliable performance (risk of delay), and automation would be bought for reliability, even if the man worked free. In this case the man's "job" is not safe even if he is superficially cheaper. A useful euphemism is "He cannot do the work" when what is meant is "He cannot be relied on to do the work."

### 1.4.2  Service Patterns

**Popular thought has related integral trains to shuttles. But the conceptual resemblance to vessels exhibits the fallacy of this limitation. Integral trains need not be shuttles any more than vessels need be ferryboats. They can run in shuttle, triangular, tramp, and other patterns. They can gather and distribute, but it is seldom, if ever, economical to use separate-car collection or distribution.**

It may be helpful to review specific service pattern possibilities.

A — *Shuttles:* A shuttle operation has only two terminals. Its train should usually be the single train that can be kept busy all of its available time — the smallest *one* train that can do the work. Shuttle operations will approach optimum only for high volumes or long distances, because small trains are seldom cheap.

*For example:* Hypothecate 1,000,000 tpy from Minnesota to Pittsburgh where attainable round-trip running time is 80 hours including delay allowance.

Terminal time is:

$$\frac{1,000,000 \times 2}{5,000} = 400 \text{ hours to load and unload at 5,000 tph}$$

Train service time will average 4 hours per trip, making total trip time 84 hours.

Monthly service: allow 16 hours for periodic maintenance, total $16 \times 12 = 192$ hours per year

| | | |
|---|---|---|
| Total hours in a year | | 8,760 |
| Terminal time | 400 | |
| Monthly service time | 192 | 592 |
| | | 8,168 |

Number of trips possible:

$$\frac{8,168}{84} = 96$$

Train size:

$$\frac{1,000,000}{96} = 10,400 \text{ tons}$$

As earlier noted, hardware choices will be biased in favor of faster cycles — even this small train will have a time value of close to $100 per hour. So . . . more engines, better brakes, etc.

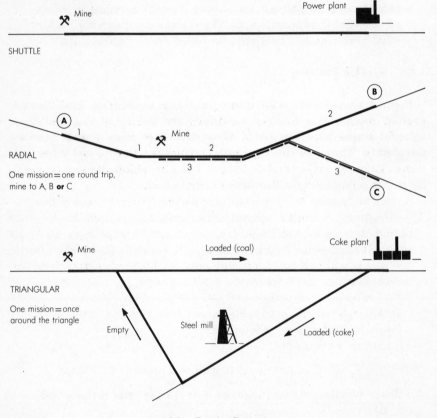

**1.4.2 — Service Patterns**

A shuttle is the simplest, but high integral train productivity usually leads to selecting some other pattern to keep it busy. A radial system —— either a delivery truck as in the sketch or a market basket — e.g., a blast furnace material train — usually is more economic. This is true because such systems can supply enough work to keep a sizable outfit busy. A triangular service will often be economic despite its double crew cost. All composite systems involve compromises — e.g., cars designed for more than one product. No reliable mechanistic selection formula is available.

B — *Radial:* The train can run radial missions, gathering or distributing. Initial size computations proceed much like the foregoing example, though with several additional variables. In this system there is a further area of choice in planning train service. It is sometimes economic for segments of the train to be rotated out of service for maintenance during a round trip of a shortened train instead of planning mechanical service as a single time allotment.

C — *Triangular:* Triangular services or other diverse routes require caution because most railroad union agreements produce double crew payments when the train does not return on the same route. This condition does not of itself exclude diverse routing — it is another and sometimes large variable.

D — *Tramp:* Such a train is dispatched like a taxicab. Few such operations are expected to arise for some time to come because of institutional barriers. They must await the appearance of an entrepreneur who will trip-lease trains like taxis.

Many trades are of such low density as to offer opportunity to find other use for the train. In the first foregoing example, the first-derived train size is small, and the possibility of finding another user to share the train should be investigated. A larger train, possibly of 20,000 + tons, would then make alternate trips in each service.

### 1.4.3 Management

**System management must be guided by a commercially oriented individual. Putting a lifelong operating man in charge usually frustrates commercial objectives and tends to make train-running an end in itself.**

*For example:* For a long time railroads promoted entirely from within the industry, and more often than not promoted operating men for various reasons. The results are what any student of modern management would expect. Performance criteria relate to "production" and not to profit.

An integral train system exists to reduce total carriage costs — whether a shipper or a railroad paid the planner. In the one case the purpose of cost reduction is to develop savings to be divided when negotiating lower rates. In the other case the objective of reducing costs is to widen profit margins or to make a profit at the lower rates that can get (or hold) the traffic.

These are both sources of contention in operation-oriented railroad management. Two discredited notions — "Get the cars, profit will take care of itself" and "We have the traffic, why all the changes?" — are still believed and must be the subject of an education program wherever found.

### 1.4.4 Division "Philosophy"

Discussion of divisions usually accompanies rate-making. After a program has been designed and budgeted, deciding which items are "in the rate" and each division thereof consists of dividing up the job — and the investments and the profits. For the foreseeable future it appears that management control — and usually at least nominal tool ownership — is best left with users. All who serve it, including those who rent it money and man its trains, will be service contractors.

For example, an integral train budget may have these items, classified as indicated. Column "A" includes those for which there is no choice but to include them in work the railroad does. Column "B" includes those for which there is no practical choice but for patrons to do the work. Column "C" includes those items that can be furnished either by the railroad or by the patrons or by both. Deciding where to put them affects:

A — The "rate" (defined as the charge the *railroad* makes).

B — The responsibility for management.

| Item | Total annual cost | | |
|---|---|---|---|
| | A | B | C |
| Train IATI | | | 1,000,000 |
| Incremental track maintenance | $ 27,000 | | |
| Train crews | 198,000 | | |
| Dispatchers, signalmen, etc. | 13,000 | | |
| Train operation crews on patron premises | | | 22,000 |
| IATI, fixed patron plant | | $230,000 | |
| Patron plant force used in loading and unloading | | 12,000 | |
| Locomotive fuel and supplies | | | 341,000 |
| Train mechanical work | | | 113,000 |
| Totals | $238,000 | $242,000 | $1,476,000 |

These costs must all be met first, wherever found and regardless of who does each bit of work. Most of the budget, characteristically, is in column "C." Policy must decide whether each item in Column "C" is supplied by the railroad and hence in the regulated rate or supplied by a patron and not in the "rate."

In this example the total outlays (incremental costs) are $1,956,000. The total "rate equivalent" is whatever the traffic will bear — more than $1,956,000 or there is no project. Regardless of who does the work represented by each item, these costs are a first claim on gross revenues or equivalent. A rate or division conference is concerned with how the excess of gross over incremental cost is divided. What each participant does with his "share" of that excess is external to the question.

In this example, if the volume is 1,000,000 tpy and the sale *value* of the *total* service (load, carry, unload, maintain surge piles, etc.) is $3 per ton, there is $1,044,000 per year available for division. Any change from the designed equipment choice and operating regime will increase the incremental cost and reduce this sum. Each "rate" or division is the pertinent part of incremental cost plus a negotiated ·division of $1,044,000 per year.

## 1.5 Procurement

An integral train system must procure services, tools, and supplies. Labor agreements whereby certain groups of employees "own" certain tracks dictate the source and price of train-drivers. All else is subject to usual commercial open-market procurement. There is nothing "special" about any supplier.

> *For example:* Someone always says, "Do you mean engines, too?" The correct reply is "Yes, until we can run without them," or "We said trains, not cars."

To pursue this example, procuring engines locally demands excessive and duplicating standby capacity. That railroads have traditionally supplied fuel oil and car wheels does not make them the preferred source. Planners must study each requirement separately — "package deals" are no more infallible in this field than in any other.

### 1.5.1 Procurement Criteria

The lowest responsible bidder concept is sound here as elsewhere, though formal processes are not usual. The criteria are economic, but planners must carefully include *all* relevant costs in their comparisons.

> *For example:* Minimizing yard or transfer crew costs will usually delay the train until time charges exceed the labor cost saving. Minimum total cost, in effect, buys more labor to save equipment, in this case. But both must be quantified and in the same budget scope.

Examples can be diversified and multiplied, but the principal caution is to avoid compartmentalized thinking that inhibits comparisons. A few examples will illustrate:

> *Station gear* — e.g., a faster conveyor belt — usually is an alternative to more cars and engines because a high-capacity belt can shorten train cycle times.

> The relation between *facility capability* and train labor is usually discontinuous. For example, a facility that will get the

train out of the territory in 8 hours instead of 10 will save 3 hours (the 2 hours is overtime) of yard crew pay, but further time reduction will save no crew labor. It will save train time, though.

Engine *fuel* is an alternative (usually a bargain) to higher maintenance resulting from start-stop operation.

The most reliable procedure is to compute total cost (regardless of where or by whom components are incurred) on an incremental cost basis and compare totals.

## 1.5.2 Allocation

Here, as elsewhere, the practice of allocating orders (traffic) is usually costly. The cost may be warranted — e.g., by reciprocity, prejudice, or personal obligations — but it should be known and evaluated. There will usually be *one* most economical route or scheme, and all departures have a price. In an integral train system the most economical choice is usually clear, and this goldfish-bowl condition is the source of some of both the support and the opposition.

To illustrate this point, hypothecate a most economic route and an alternate with a longer minimum attainable running time. If the shipper insists on allocation, the capital cost can be projected thus (train size for each route calculated as previously outlined):

Required train size, using most economic route, 15,000 tons.

Required train size, using alternate route, 18,000 tons.

If half the traffic is run on one route and half on the other, the train size will be *about* 16,500 tons. The increased 1,500 tons capacity (at 1967 costs) will cost about $750,000 in capital. There will also be additional operating costs — e.g., distance costs. Any action that incurs avoidable cost — e.g., allocation — will reduce the amount of profit available for division. The total *value* of transportation performed will not change, but incremental costs will increase.

Furthermore, arbitrary allocation among routes usually adds more parties to divide the smaller available sum. Some hold that the very visibility of integral train system costs is reason for suppressing such computations — they are alleged to inhibit the "deals." It should not be necessary to belabor the point that a railroad with a second-choice route can compete only by accepting a smaller contribution to overhead and profit. This is not new, but integral train systems quantify the phenomenon — often painfully so.

Planners must normally estimate some such difference to answer the inevitable questions. Planners encountering otherwise inexplicable resistances may explore this area for reasons.

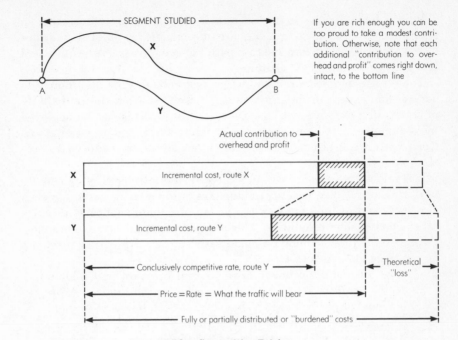

If you are rich enough you can be too proud to take a modest contribution. Otherwise, note that each additional "contribution to overhead and profit" comes right down, intact, to the bottom line

### 1.5.2 — Competitive Pricing

One route may seem less costly on the basis of fully distributed costs, but it may actually be more costly on incremental costs. At any price the line with the lower incremental costs will earn a higher contribution to overhead and profit — even when the price leaves one of them with a negative contribution. Either line wants the business at any level it can get that will yield *a* contribution to overhead and profit, but one line can set a conclusive price if it elects to do so — and if the competitor is astute enough to know when he is losing money. So long as the "rate" agreed to by ostensibly competing carriers is high enough to produce some net for the weakest, then allocation is acceptable and only the railroads lose thereby — the shipper in such cases could not care less.

## 1.5.3 Accessory Services

**Primary choices involve route, equipment and fuel. Secondary choices involve loading gear, communications systems, and others. For small items reliability values justify superficially uneconomic choices. Reliability, related to delay allowances and the dominant time values, is, itself, an important economic element.**

Reliability appears in economic computations in the form of delay allowances. There is no available reliability data for most railway gear. Quantitative reliability measurement as understood in military or similar circles is unknown in railroad equipment circles. Therefore planners must judge from available data in assigning delay allowances and maintenance time.

Pull-in maintenance is not adequate. Neither is over-designing in ignorance. Both of these practices are uneconomic for different reasons. The planner must tread a narrow path between gross over-equipment and a "hope for the best" attitude.

The planner's objective is to budget just enough time and money to assure that, except in the most unusual circumstances, the probability of completing each mission is close to certainty. This can be achieved by redundancy, frequent preventive maintenance, and in other ways. Comparisons can be made *only* after alternatives are reduced to economic equivalency.

It is seldom practical to assign a direct value to reliability or penalty to unreliability. The practical procedure is to estimate costs, for each alternate, and include enough equipment and maintenance to produce satisfactory system reliability. This procedure automatically eliminates those systems that cannot be made satisfactory. The ritual need not be completed in every case.

> *For example:* Ordinary open journal bearings will seldom survive analysis. They cannot be made to produce an acceptable level of performance. They can, at best, be made to yield about 2,500,000 car-miles between failures. An economic-size integral train will comprise some 250 to 300 cars, so that open journals will produce one road failure every 10,000 train-miles — once in 3 weeks at 500 miles per day. Clearly this is unsatisfactory, and no attempt at evaluating is warranted—open journals are simply unsatisfactory. The consequent spare equipment would cost more than reliable (roller or cartridge) bearings. And the costs of "if and when" service.

## 1.6 Applications

Where transportation is needed an integral train system may be the lowest-cost available tool. It may also be alternative to a non-transportation choice such as decentralization. It usually will weight decentralization choices in favor of modernization instead of relocation.

Integral trains may be used as "market baskets" or "delivery wagons." They can gather and disperse. They can mix and blend. They can handle bulk and general cargo (containerized). They can be trip-leased (like vessels) and so be shared among several users. They can be dispatched like taxicabs or run like buses. They can handle commonplace cargoes or freight that conventional trains could not satisfactorily carry at all.

> *For example:* A hot slag train is a species of integral train, and the steel industry contains several places where long-distance hot-metal trains could develop important economies.

Planners are cautioned to introduce the integral train alternative early. Its generally uncomprehended terminal locational flexibility and ability to serve dispersed markets can often be turned to strategic advantage. Opportunities escape if plans are allowed to crystalize before "seeing if an integral train can be used." Self-serving advice can be hazardous here as elsewhere.

*For example:* Railroad-employed "experts" advised a power company that integral trains could not be interlined for reasons "too complex to explain to a nonrailroader." And for "highly technical" reasons they could only run from certain mining regions to only a few plant sites. The railroad owned all the coal land from which the train "could" run and none of the destinations that "could" be served was available to competitive service. They were acting "commercially" but a consultant could offer the power company little help after the deal had been closed.

### 1.6.1 Market Baskets and Delivery Wagons

These services will usually run radials — one cargo of one commodity (or a few commodities) to or from one or a few points each trip. They will seldom carry the same commodity or traverse the same route on successive trips. For each mission there is one best route and all trips on that mission will use it.

Radial services usually require design compromises. For example, if one route has a light bridge, it is usually wise to investigate routes with fewer limits — each route normally is used infrequently.

System design starts with train size. As in the shuttle case, terminal time is first estimated. Running-time determination is more complex because there are several routes. This step proceeds thusly: (Variants may arise with, for example, commodities of widely differing densities.)

Hypothecate 1,000,000 tpy as follows
    200,000 to (or from) destination A = 20%
    300,000 to (or from) destination B = 30%
    500,000 to (or from) destination C = 50%
Terminal time will be estimated thus:
    1,000,000 tpy @ 5,000 tph (common station) = 200 hr/yr
    1,000,000 tpy @ 3,300 tph (satellite stations) = 300 hr/yr
    Servicing @ 2 shifts per month: 16 x 12    = 192 hr/yr
                            Total   692 hr/yr

Time available for running:   8,760
              less   692
                    8,068 hr/yr

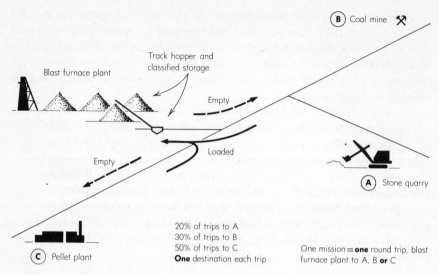

Blast furnace plant

Track hopper and classified storage

B Coal mine

Empty

Loaded

Empty

A Stone quarry

C Pellet plant

20% of trips to A
30% of trips to B
50% of trips to C
**One** destination each trip

One mission = **one** round trip, blast furnace plant to A, B **or** C

### 1.6.1 — A "Market Basket" System

A train owned by, say, a blast furnace plant will use mechanically compromised cars for various commodities. It takes a large plant to keep one train busy, such is their productivity. Alternatively and usually more economically, a group of plants could, jointly, use a coal train, a pellet train and a stone train.

Round-trip running times, including delay and terminal *trip service* (not loading and unloading) is:

| | |
|---|---|
| To destination A | 22 hr |
| To destination B | 39 hr |
| To destination C | 58 hr |

Let N = number of trips per year

$$22 \times 0.20 \times N + 39 \times 0.30 \times N + 58 \times 0.50 \times N = 8{,}068$$
$$4.4 \times N + 11.8 + 29.0 \times N = 8{,}068$$
$$N = \frac{8{,}068}{45.2} = 168 \text{ trips/yr}$$

Train size is

$$\frac{1{,}000{,}000}{168} = 6{,}000 \text{ tons}$$

This general procedure derives the size of train that can be kept busy. In this example, chosen for illustration, a larger train to minimize crew costs (among other reasons) should be reviewed — a 6,000-ton train is very small. In reviewing a larger train three alternatives should be studied:

A — Find some other use for the idle time — i.e., more business.

B — Allow the train to stand idle when not in use or reduce station investment to lengthen station time.

C — Under-power the train to cut capital cost and lengthen its schedule — which usually involves consequential delays that are difficult to estimate and costly to pay for.

There is no substitute for ingenuity in finding economies.

## 1.6.2 Distribution, Gathering, and the Like

**Gathering and distribution are usually best performed by the whole train making successive stops, using fast loading and unloading systems. Switching, placing, and reassembling cars is seldom economical. A "marketplace" operation is simply a gathering system on one side and a distribution system on the other side of a warehouse.**

A wheat gathering application will illustrate. Hypothecate a 9,000-ton cargo, not uniformly distributed among 13 elevators. A time computation makes it clear that the usual scheme (dispersing and recovering cars) is more costly. Of course the user of the train must buy his cargo from elevators chosen with due regard to routing. Any one cargo should be loaded at elevators on a rational route; other trips will serve other shippers and other changes.

Loading time computation:

$$\frac{9,000 \text{ tons}}{90} = 100 \text{ cars (covered hoppers)}$$

Loading rate used is 15 minutes per car, load in discharge order to make the desired blend — car order will not be disturbed after loading.

Loading time will be

$$\frac{100 \times 15}{60} = 25 \text{ hours}$$

Hypothecate a distribution of the 13 elevators over a route 300 miles long, much of it low-speed track. Running time in the loading area is 300 @ 25 mph or 12 hours.

Allow a delay time of 10% + of the total, or 3 hours.

The *total* time (loaded and empty) to gather the grain over 300 miles is 40 train-hours or an average of

$$\frac{40}{24} = 1.67 \text{ car-days per car}$$

Loading such a train will use about 8 engine units (including spare) for 40 hours or $8 \times 40 = 320$ engine-unit-hours to handle 100 loads and 100 empties or 0.6 "cars" per engine-unit-hour. But these engines get 24 *effective* hours per day, whereas an industry average is about 8 hours in 24. An equivalent productivity in conventional operation would be 1.8 "cars" per engine-*unit*-hour — and is seldom attained. (Half that is usual.)

Loading the train will use 4 (theoretically 3) crew-days plus overtime, equivalent to, at worst, 7 crew-days' pay or 56 *paid* hours, handling 100 loads and 100 empties or 3.6 "cars" per paid crew-hour.

In contrast consider the number of

Car-days

Engine-unit-hours

Crew-hours

that would be required to run 300 miles of secondary line, place 100 empties and recover, yard and dispatch 100 loads — and inspect, which the integral train does not need.

Such variations as layer loading, random-car loading and the like can be devised. Train size selection for such cases must be a "cut and try" operation, assisted by the designer's experience and judgment.

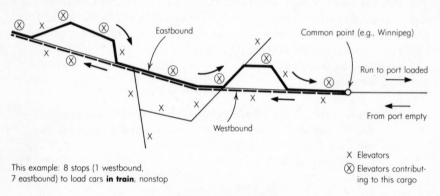

This example: 8 stops (1 westbound, 7 eastbound) to load cars **in train**; nonstop

X Elevators
Ⓧ Elevators contributing to this cargo

#### 1.6.2 — Wheat-Gathering Routes

In this Canadian prairie example, wheat for one cargo should be bought from a series of country elevators that can be served in a practical sequence — note one stop outbound and several inbound. Economy is compromised if a cargo must contain wheat from elevators on parallel routes that require "backtracking" or yarding.

### 1.6.3 General Cargo

General cargo systems will almost always involve containers, unitizing, palletizing, or similar. In this group of applications the train itself keeps moving, handling containers in short station stops or serving only major points with whole-train or large block deliveries for supplemental highway movement. The traditional practice of leaving individual cars to be loaded and reassembled is costly.

Integral train general cargo systems will normally use specialized, skeletonized container cars with a side-transfer system. At the present writing no cases have been found in which cranes are economic — and some very high volume cases have been studied.

There are two basic cases:

A — Cases in which one or a few containers are set off at each of many way stations, with a side-transfer truck servicing the train as at a passenger stop.

B — Cases in which self-contained, self powered permanently coupled car blocks are set off at selected concentration points for either truck dispersal or branchline movement (economically isolated from through movement).

The first case will seldom arise — given the rising sophistication of truck distribution. In estimating applicability of case "A," it is best to plan for two 20-foot containers on a single transfer cycle which will take about 8 minutes and require a truck equipped with side-transfer hardware.

At major stations *or* where long goods are to be handled, a system of multiple containers or pallets up to 80 feet long can be used. Similarly, autos can be handled on bilevel "containers" up to 80 feet long. The transfer unit in such cases will be an 80-foot truck or trailer equipped to side-transfer four 20-foot units at once, with a nominal capacity of 90 tons. Such a unit is an off-highway tool with a gross loaded weight of about 120 to 130 tons.

When alternative "B" is used the station will use 80-foot transfer units. Block size is governed by these criteria:

One train block should effectively use one power plant (or a pair) and a tank car. A popular arrangement will employ about 2,500 to 3,000 hp to handle 50 (20-foot) container units on 11 80-foot trailer cars and 2 80-foot powered cars, of which 20 feet is a machinery compartment. Such a block has no separate locomotive. Any block should be loaded for only one station.

The two systems should not be combined in one operation. If both services (A and B) are to be supplied on one route it will usually be advisable to run them separately.

There will be instances in which entire container blocks can be loaded, still aboard the cars at one traffic source. For example, a producer of nonferrous concentrates can load a full block of 50 open-top containers from storage while the rest of the train goes on to the end of its line and returns. All such cases should be planned for specific schedules. The philosophy of free time and random schedules is not often applicable or even acceptable.

## 1.6.4 "Common Carriers"

Integral trains can be treated as "big cars" or self-propelled big cars commercially analogous to trucks or vessels. An operator can sell them on a time or trip basis.

*For example:* A certain power company can profitably use 80% of the capability of the integral train that could produce its transportation most economically. It can afford to pay as much for that 80% as it could for exclusive use of a train — it only wants its coal hauled. An operator could trip-lease the remaining 20% of the train's time to other customers.

There are two variations of such an operation:

A — An operator may own one or several whole trains and trip-lease them like taxicabs, charging time and mileage.

B — Self-propelled car blocks for either containers or bulk can be run at the head end of scheduled trains for the long trips. They can run separately on branch lines or elsewhere when the time/crew cost relationships so indicate and it is not still cheaper to truck from a "gateway."

### 1.6.5 Joint, Special, etc.

**A wide variety of unique combined, joint, and/or special operations can be devised.**

For example, an external fixed cycle may modulate a composite system. A circular or diverse route will be more costly because train crews must be duplicated (this is substantially true of conventional trains, but the fact is difficult to conceal in integral train system planning, thus illuminating a commercially central characteristic). Back-hauls, off-route deliveries and other specifics will be found in the array of "specials."

Operations in this group are, by definition, special or unique. It is not practical to treat the possibilities exhaustively, since they are limited only by the diversity of requirements and the ingenuity of designers.

### 1.7 Cost Estimating

**Cost relationships are not always systematic or continuous and planners must proceed much as a contractor estimates a building. "Experience" or "average" costs seldom apply in specific cases and they inhibit the search for low-cost innovations by denying their effect. Each program is unique and there is no substitute for detailed estimating.**

Estimators will find — as building estimators have long known — that even when an estimator is not himself knowledgeable in every specialty (few are), a conscientious effort to estimate in detail will produce good results. Problems arise when too-large segments are attempted.

Despite the fact that cost elements vary with time, distance, tonnage, number of trips, and other variables, time costs will dominate.

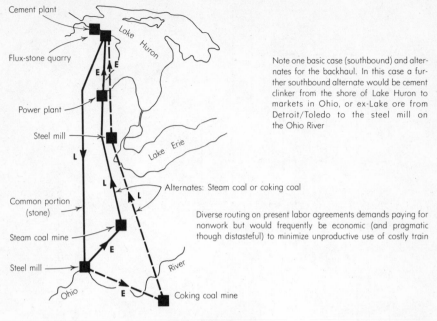

Note one basic case (southbound) and alternates for the backhaul. In this case a further southbound alternate would be cement clinker from the shore of Lake Huron to markets in Ohio, or ex-Lake ore from Detroit/Toledo to the steel mill on the Ohio River

Alternates: Steam coal or coking coal

Diverse routing on present labor agreements demands paying for nonwork but would frequently be economic (and pragmatic though distasteful) to minimize unproductive use of costly train

### 1.6.5 — Joint Services

This sketch shows one example of a composite service in which a single train can perform individual missions for various customers in turn. It is intended to suggest that composite use by several customers will often prove economic. An extension of this premise is the "for hire" train. The presence of alternatives is typical of such plans.

## 1.7.1   Kinds of Costs

**The largest cost is capital cost — related to investment. Operating costs are largely fuel, wheels, and crew wages — and a long list of small items. System costs are incurred by an integral train system and are not directly related to specific trains or functions — e.g., management of a group of trains.**

Capital costs can be estimated only after schedules, schemes, preliminary designs, etc., have established what must be bought.

The accompanying tabulation is not intended as an exhaustive check list, though it illustrates chains of related costs. There is no substitute for thorough research, because each case is unique.

The recommended operating cost estimating procedure starts with a series of in-depth interviews with operating and shipper/consignee men at all levels. The nominal, proximate and/or ostensible purpose of these interviews is to uncover all the elements of cost and associated operating limits — though it is the task of the *designer* (not the interviewee) to quantify them. These interviews also have the effect of informing

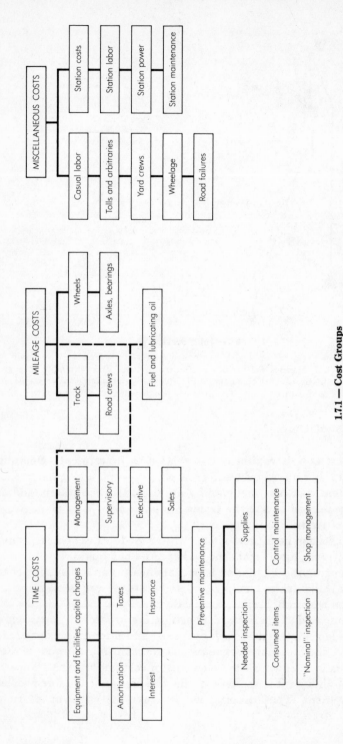

**1.7.1 — Cost Groups**

This chart indicates principal groups or "chains" of costs. It cannot list them all but it should suggest areas for inquiry.

the men who must eventually live with the system and "involving" them in its design. A knowledgeable and active designer soon accumulates a fund of data more extensive and varied than that of any railroader.

Planners will do well to verify that each of the listed elements has been considered but are also well advised to avoid assuming that there are no others. Men inexperienced in integral train planning can usefully work in teams of two men, one of whom is skilled or experienced in industrial systems or work analysis but totally uninformed about railroading.

## 1.7.2  Cost Bases

An integral train budget is a series of terms in an equation: so many elapsed hours — moving, standing, working, delayed, it makes no difference — times an hourly imputed rent, plus so many miles times a rate for road crews and another for wheels, so many inspections, yard crews and taxicabs times the price of each, and so on. To budget a specific program one must thoroughly examine the operation for items that might be overlooked. Traditional accounting will help but little, if at all. One starts with the jobs to be done, in detail.

If the work is done thoroughly the planner will have a list, in some detail, of functions that must be performed and will have extensive notes about *how* each can be carried out.

Budgeting is then simply a matter of bookkeeping. It is usually best arranged in the usual "invoice" form:

Quantity              Item              Unit      Unit cost*      Total
*Estimated *by planner*, using any information he can find.

A useful variation is to provide more than one column under the "total" heading so that costs imputed to railroads generally or individual railroads, shippers and others can be carried down separately.

It is sound practice to develop a derivation for each unit cost *for each project* until a planner gains experience — and even then some unit costs will vary surprisingly from project to project. It is unsound to rely on unit costs from other projects for anything but preliminary projections.

Planners will find the following cost categories dominate most budgets:

    Capital service  (IATI)
    Fuel and supplies
    Crew  wages
    Mechanical maintenance (of which wheel/axle work is a large
        fraction)

The following groups will include most second-level cost categories:
Terminal ownership and operation
Routine fueling and mechanical servicing
Management, sales and supervision
The large number of individually minor costs are important for two reasons:
They total large in some cases (but not many)
They offer critics an opportunity for nit-picking (often for unworthy objectives) if neglected or lumped together
These minor costs include, among others:
Track maintenance
Dispatchers, towermen and the like
Inspectors (needed and "nominal")
"Pilots"
Ownership and maintenance of roadway improvements

## 1.8 Financing

**When capital costs are treated as imputed rent, before profits or savings are claimed, it makes little difference how the program is financed.**
When a shipper finances the train, the rate of return used is the one that prevails in his business — where his alternate investment opportunities exist. For a railroad to finance it, the same basis is used, with a reservation. Carrier men's notorious vulnerability to shipper demands to "give me one, too" will usually lead to shipper financing, precipitated by *superficially* arbitrary railroad refusal to finance — thus excluding the shipper who cannot use an integral train system effectively. In any case entire systems must be planned so that money in all components can be compared when making design decisions. Divisions come later.

### 1.8.1 Own or Lease

**A choice among methods of borrowing money must be made for any investment. However, financing and servicing should be separately evaluated. A "full service" lease is not always best, and it has an inherent disadvantage in that dissimilar functions are combined.**
*For example:* A car company insisted on quoting lease terms — its manufacturing arm did not want to sell. Then it learned that the mileage in integral train service would be 11 times the "normal" and the car might not outlast its lease. The car company depended on the value of the car after the user buys it — and gives it back.

Many corporate economists erroneously treat car leases as if the money were of a different kind from that involved in other leases — e.g., fixed plant.

The system planner's principal problem is conveying understanding of the notion that money is money and such devices as finance leasing are equivalent to loans — and comparable regardless of the nature of the asset. Only in this way can the freedom to compare different *kinds* of costs be retained. The problem is one of communication and is made difficult by an array of fixed ideas.

### 1.8.2  Fixed System Plant

**An integral train system may require (in the interest of *its own* economy) assorted, usually small, railroad plant betterments. They are designed and budgeted as if they were the property of the integral train system because they are alternatives to such choices as train equipment, station capability, etc. Choosing their supplier is part of the dividing-up process and comes later.**

It will come as a shock to some to learn that fixed plant betterments on railroad property are part of the capital budget for an integral train system — often shipper-owned and shipper-financed. The rationale starts with an uncompromising concern with balance sheets. If a specific improvement can be paid for from the time savings of the integral trains, it should be in the integral train budget and the base schedule should be for the improved line. Don't pay for it twice.

> *For example:* A section of track will be traversed three times a week, each way. Train time is worth $6 per minute. *One* minute of transit time saving per trip is worth
>
> $$3 \times 2 \times \$6 \times 52 = \$1,872 \text{ per year}$$
>
> If IATI is 15% (a not-uncommon figure for long-life track improvement), the capital that can be spent to produce 1 minute (per trip) in transit time saving is
>
> $$\frac{1,872}{0.15} = \$12,500$$
>
> Such an improvement might be smoother track for higher speed (e.g., 60 mph from 50 at *one* switch for a 5-mile train) or others of many kinds of low-budget improvements.

If a prospective track project will not pay out on the savings to the integral train system *alone* it is better to let the railroad decide whether to carry it out or not. The railroad can apply the time-bonus money the project can earn from the integral train system plus any other available benefits to other traffic to determine whether to make the investment or not — when it knows how to calculate time benefits to other traffic. One assumes nothing.

### 1.8.3 Fixed Patron Plant

Integral train systems usually include station facilities — e.g., hoppers, tracks and conveyors. These facilities, wherever located, should be designed and budgeted as the property of the integral train system — regardless of their eventual "ownership." Thus choices between, for example, more train and more station can be resolved rationally. When divisions are determined prematurely, each party resists providing anything; and antieconomic choices result.

It will be traumatic for some to find patron plant included in train budgets. The usual device used to achieve an essentially artificial separation is a tariff-stated "free time," below which there is no incentive to secure further time economy. Such "free time" is then negotiated in a vacuum and no system design occurs.

The relationship can be illustrated by a coal loading plant computation.

Hypothecate 300,000 tpy of coal and a train that is worth $4.00 per minute

A loading belt capable of 3,000 tph is taken as the base case — it will work 100 hours per year, and the *minimum* conveyor system that will do the job and hold together for the amortization period (in this case about 1,000 hours) must be planned (light belt, high speeds, etc.)

A loading belt capable of 5,000 tph can load the coal in 60 hours per year, saving 40 train-hours per year

The value of the train time saved will be

$40 \times \$4.00 \times 60 = \$9,600$ per year

If IATI is 20% (not uncommon for station gear), the supportable *additional* cost of the faster belt is

$$\frac{9,600}{0.20} = \$48,000$$

Such capability increases will be justified surprisingly often. But the computation is correct only when operating conditions permit using the faster turnaround. Note that no labor saving is projected — employees get 1 day per trip anyway.

### 1.9 Pricing

Ratemaking is a policymaker's process. However, the planner must understand some of the considerations involved. One is the fact that traditional rate and price relationships and even definitions are often not relevant or informative.

*For example:* An integral train "rate" is meaningless except for a specific set of physically significant conditions. It covers only what the railroad does or supplies. **Transferring such an item as car ownership from the railroad to the shipper reduces the "rate" but does not of itself change the cost — though many public pronouncements have so implied.**

It is useful to think of ratemaking as a process whereby policy men divide the entire operation, including its capital and its profits, among the participants *after* it is designed. Engineering bakes and measures the "pie." Policy divides it. Planners should refuse to discuss prices and divisions of money or responsibilities prematurely — if only because most of their hearers will incorrectly translate the resulting numbers into traditional frameworks.

*For example:* One man said "I dare not tell anyone how many lampposts there are on Broadway lest some traffic man think it's a freight rate."

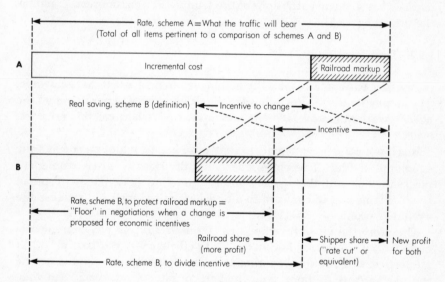

Hypothesis: Neither railroad nor shipper can, physically, convert from A to B without at least the consent of the other

**1.9.1 — Prices and Divisions**

Most integral train schemes require physical adaptations in which shipper and railroad must concur. Hence savings must be divided. If the railroad is going to get the traffic anyway, its markup must reflect this fact in dividing the savings. Obviously "it does *not* begin with a rate."

## 1.9.1  Price Levels

The *total* price charged for transportation is presumably established like any other price — what the traffic will bear. It is thus usually limited by available competitive systems and reflects actual or supposed differences in value of service among alternatives. But all the computations are only attempts to help guess what the traffic will bear — pragmatically — independently of cost.

If that operating regime is chosen that results in the lowest total incremental cost, the sum available for contributions to overhead and profit is maximized whether it is correctly estimated or not. Distribution is another matter.

In this context the total "saving" to the shipper (compared with other available systems) is part of the "profit" that is divided — including inplant handling savings, for example.

Presentation and negotiation strategies are external to *this* analysis. This statement is made with full awareness of the sensitive nature of many such negotiations. It is also made with full awareness of the fact that the "rates" and publicly stated "costs" will consist in large part of more or less arbitrary divisions of the totals. (For commercial exploitation see chapter 4.)

### 1.9.2 Divisions

Division rationale, especially among railroads, must be economic. The money that is available for division is what is left *after* doing all the needed work at lowest *total* (incremental) cost, wherever this criterion leads.

It is less costly, for example, to centralize engine maintenance and the supplying of fuel. Therefore traditional divisions of gross would not please the line with the service station. Spending more money to spread the functions and so conform to a division philosophy only reduces the available profit.

Therefore the gross revenue must be used, first, to pay incremental costs (using a formula that motivates to efficiency — no "cost plus") of all parties, without any "overheads." The rest must be divided among the participants as their policymakers negotiate, and each can then apply his division to overhead or martinis if he likes. Any departure from the lowest-total-incremental-cost design will reduce the amount of money available for division — even if the departure does make the operation fit traditional costing methods.

# 2. TECHNOLOGY

Engineering design is a series of economic choices, each directed to reducing total incremental costs independently of divisions of savings. Equipment and components are used to the limits of their realistic capability; all "better" schemes are subject to value analysis. Longevity-type designs (where capital buys little but long life) seldom survive investment criteria, because recovery of incremental capital is too slow. Little or no reliance can be placed on longevity-type designs, conceived either to sell hardware or in ignorance of investment criteria. The engineer must be resourceful and largely self-sufficient, since his customer's interest in low capital cost is adverse to most vendors'. He must be rigorously objective and wholly committed to economic objectives. His philosophy approaches "once it *does* the job, cheapest is best." Much of his effort is devoted to determining which is *really* cheapest. Men from the structural field will recognize some concepts of what they have called "limit design." Others will recognize the commercially oriented engineer's phrase "Anybody can do it with money."

An engineer who studies the design of integral train systems will be impressed with an unremitting concern with money. Especially so the "organization man" designer — he has spent his life designing to "standards," piling safety factor on safety factor, seeking long life for its own sake and seeking the "best." He will find value analysis traumatic.

*For example:* A conveyor that gets 300 to 500 hours of service per year, budgeted on a 10-year amortization, can use lightweight belt, overloaded motors, prelubricated bearings, and high speeds that would limit continuous service to less than a year. Conveyor vendors will seek to discourage him for obvious reasons and will not "hold his hand." Buying more cars just to keep a conveyor busy is wasteful, but is done.

The intended orientation is to the user's pocketbook. Historically most American basic industry engineering has been paid for from hardware sales budgets. Hence, for example, the American slow conveyor practice compared to high European conveyor speeds. Hence, the tendency to use complex, hence often unreliable and costly devices for simple tasks.

*For example:* A tunnel gate with a manual or hydraulic operator will use few working parts, all accessible, to feed a belt — cheaper *and* more reliably than a battery of feeders. It does *not* follow that reliability costs more money. The "gadget" that is not there need not be dualized for reliability, to cite one manifestation.

Every choice is based on money. For example, a train's time does not concern the traditional station designer because his frame of reference isolates this cost. It is important — and visibly so — in integral train system design. Most of the "intangibles" in this context favor simple devices in the interest of reliability, because unreliability costs train time — which is money in the form of delay allowances.

> *For example:* Concern for train-time cost and avoidance of costly consequential delays will nearly always lead to overpowering and using in-train power unit spares. Another example: Controlled maintenance is an illustration of quality *and* low cost, not quality *vs.* low cost. Still another example: A sealed unit is not "denied the service of wayside repairmen," it is protected from wayside "repairmen," and the wayside service cost does not then appear on the budget.

Cost orientation also affects train design. Investment is directly related to cycle length, figured in hours and minutes, not days — there are few places where whole days can be found. Seeking the available small time savings is wholly new to a man who previously thought of time in days only, if at all. In consequence many individually minor railroad plant improvements are important to an integral train but are incorrectly considered inconsequential in conventional railroading where time savings are less visible.

> *For example:* At a certain division point about 15 minutes could be saved, each way, by using electric locks and negotiating a crew run-through. The superintendent said a conventional train could not be trusted without a mechanical check at this point but an integral train would be another matter. Besides, no one counted 15 minutes for conventional trains.

Estimating attainable cycle times is an art in which comprehension of operating problems is combined with engineering capability and ability to evaluate what people say and mean. The preoccupation with money relates to the fact that train time *is* money — usually as much as all the rest of the pertinent costs combined. Problems arise because many operating men have seen past improvements frustrated by insistence that "new" trains be compromised to suit obsolete equipment and methods.

The notion of what *can* be done is usually difficult to get across. It is sometimes necessary to belabor the obvious point that superior — not always more costly — equipment can produce superior performance.

> *For example:* A railroad research department commented on an integral train report. It said: "The consultant's cost projections are lower than our historic costs. We found that his recommended operating regimes differ from our practice. When we standardized the operating regimes, the costs agreed

with our experience and proved that we cannot profitably compete for this traffic."

An integral train system design study must devote considerable space to outlining the recommended equipment and operating regime lest its readers assume that the program is just a "rate gimmick."

## 2.1 Terminals

**"Terminals" in this context are facilities used to load and unload trains. This definition is quite different from others often used, and planners must verify that terminology is correctly used.**

Such terminals traditionally are patron responsibilities. Transportation companies traditionally concern themselves only with "free time" rules, leaving but limited incentive to plan or operate terminals for best *total* cost. Incommensurability of shipper's and carrier's money leads to waste.

Terminal planning is *part* of system planning. Planners must explain the relationships in detail to railroad management men who have spent their lives not wanting to know the "shipper's" problems. The more important relationships are:

A — Train-handling costs vary discontinuously — e.g., even a little overtime sometimes costs another crew-day; disassembling a train uses disproportionate amounts of labor.

B — Terminal time often controls cycle length. Small investments in terminal capability will often produce large reductions in train investments.

*For example:* At a power plant where a train will call biweekly, 1 hour per visit is 26 train-hours per year. For a large train worth about $500 per hour this saving can support an increased station investment of nearly $100,000. (This combination will exist at about 1,000,000 tons per year.)

*For example:* As a rule of thumb, if a train service belt is to get more than 300 service hours per year it should probably be dualized to save train time — when belt *and* train are in the same budget, so permitting such choices.

C — Terminal design often affects train design. A designer who thinks in carloads may provide a terminal that cannot unload a train as a unit. A railroader who thinks of normally motionless cars will oppose a main-track hopper. To avoid mainline "occupancy" he will require a switcher to occupy a main track for more hours than direct, one-piece mainline terminaling.

Terminal facility components are simple in concept. Time costs dominate and fast turnarounds are essential. Nonstop systems are usually best — hence usually no car dumpers. For example: In track hopper designing the first variable is not "how many at once" but how many feet the cars will travel while discharging.

The concepts are dynamic, not static. A track in "constant" use, for example, usually turns out to be about 5% used and 95% available.

*For example:* An employee access crossing should not be blocked at shift time, but an integral train can use it for several properly chosen hours with brief or no interruptions. But tradition says that cars, once placed, stand unattended; hence the mental blocks the planner must overcome.

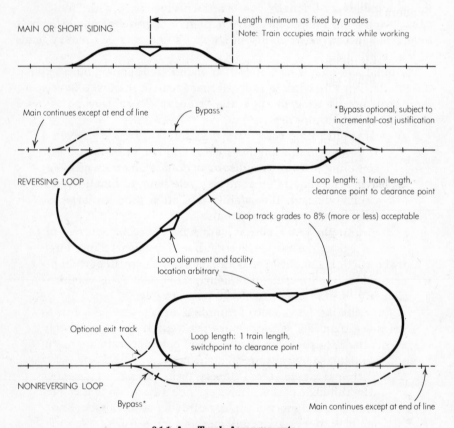

**2.1.1-A — Track Arrangements**

Most terminal arrangements are variations of those shown. The loops can exploit the ability of the integral train to negotiate short steep grades because very little of the train need be on a short grade at one time. Nonreversing loops are most adaptable to adverse grades because the entire track — downhill as well as uphill — is occupied. A loading point should ideally be at a summit and an unloading point should ideally be at a sag.

### 2.1.1 Terminal Design Criteria

A typical design regime will generate a first approximation which must be modified for each project. Train and schedule design usually force at least a two-step design procedure. The number of approximations depends on the project and the use to be made of the design study — e.g., a feasibility study starts the design but stops far short of contract drawings. Avoidance of overdesign is essential and requires vigilance, given the cultural bias of most engineers.

It is usually desirable to handle the train in one piece, though sectional handling is possible, at a price. Basic track arrangements are:

A — Main track (and variations)

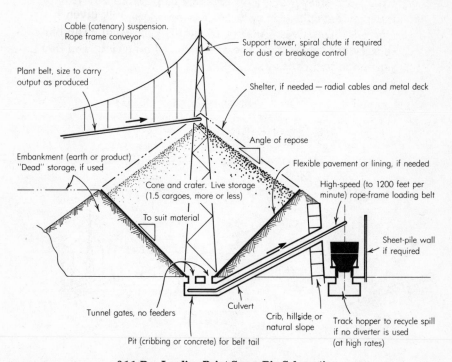

Cable (catenary) suspension. Rope frame conveyor

Support tower, spiral chute if required for dust or breakage control

Plant belt, size to carry output as produced

Shelter, if needed — radial cables and metal deck

Angle of repose

Embankment (earth or product) "Dead" storage, if used

Flexible pavement or lining, if needed

Cone and crater. Live storage (1.5 cargoes, more or less)

High-speed (to 1200 feet per minute) rope-frame loading belt

To suit material

Sheet-pile wall if required

Tunnel gates, no feeders

Culvert

Crib, hillside or natural slope

Track hopper to recycle spill if no diverter is used (at high rates)

Pit (cribbing or concrete) for belt tail

#### 2.1.1-B — Loading Point Surge Bin Schematic

Most loading facilities will be variations of this low-capital scheme until some important improvement in technology appears. An earth-fill hopper with flexible (or no) lining is virtually immune to settlement damage and so needs no special foundation. The train-loading belt will be a one-speed, high-rate conveyor with short service life. The roof, if any, will be minimum. The sheet-pile wall will be used only when the facility is close to active tracks (or a highway) and will prevent damage to passing trains or accumulation of material on adjacent tracks. The plant belt will be a clear-span rope-frame belt designed for operation whenever the plant operates. Framed bins, elevated storage, long-life conveyors, rigid galleries, mechanical feeders and the like are not only costly but some of them also diminish the utility of the plant by their exposure to mechanical failure.

B — Turnaround loops

C — Nonreversing loops

Surge pile size (loading or unloading) is related to train size. A loading station surge pile should be at least 1.5 cargoes, fed whenever the producing plant works. It may be paralleled by conventional facilities for other traffic.

An unloading station surge pile should be about 1.5 cargoes for a station with no further storage (e.g., a power plant using steam coal), or one cargo when supplementary handling is used (e.g., where the surge pile is unloaded to classified storage after each use).

Component design criteria are:.

*Track loop:* Provide just enough track to handle the whole train. A nonreversing loop, as short as possible, is virtually independent of grades up to 8% or even more.

*Surge pile:* Design is a matter of simple geometry, given the density and angle of repose of the stored material. The live portion is two cones.

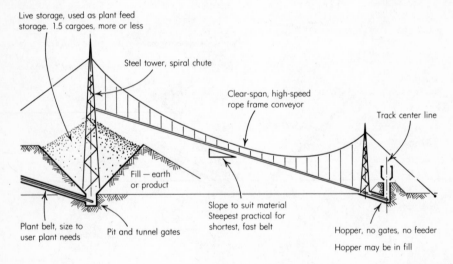

Live storage, used as plant feed storage. 1.5 cargoes, more or less

Steel tower, spiral chute

Clear-span, high-speed rope frame conveyor

Track center line

Fill — earth or product

Plant belt, size to user plant needs

Pit and tunnel gates

Slope to suit material
Steepest practical for shortest, fast belt

Hopper, no gates, no feeder

Hopper may be in fill

Note: Hopper volume or capacity is not important; hopper function is that of a chute — concept is dynamic, not static

#### 2.1.1-C — Unloading Station Schematic

The track hopper is shown in fill to avoid groundwater, taking advantage of the integral train's ability to accommodate steep grades. The hopper itself should be a chute to guide the material to the stacking belt. The stacking belt should be only long enough to reach the top of the surge pile — in a double-cone or cone-and-crater form. Clear-span rope-frame construction will usually be lowest in cost. The economic service life of this conveyor is usually limited — annual volume times amortization period divided by hourly rate. The reclaim pit will usually serve a low-rate plant feed belt and so will sometimes need a feeder, though a tunnel gate is preferred. The fill around the live storage can be the "disaster reserve" or dead storage.

*Unloading hopper and stacking belt:* Hopper length must permit nonstop unloading direct to the belt. Stacking belts must deliver material to the conical pile at the design speed — the hopper, functionally, is just a chute and the train is the feeder.

*Loading belt:* Tunnel gates and loading belt are sized for train time economy. Tilt pans or pants-leg chutes usually will be impractical at economic rates, and a track hopper will be used to recycle what spills between cars.

## 2.1.2 Terminal Types and Characteristics

Basic types can be functionally defined:

- A — One-source bulk loading terminals
- B — One-user bulk unloading terminals
- C — Classified bulk storage, blending and dispensing terminals
- D — Marine transfer terminals, inbound and outbound
- E — Container terminals
- F — Specialized bulk terminals

The diversity of situations compels dependence on design ingenuity — applied with an understanding of system rationale.

This subsection concerns general arrangements and design schemes. Component design is reviewed elsewhere.

### 2.1.2.1 One-Source Loading Stations

Stations in this category are typified by coal mine stations shipping homogeneous steam coal. In such stations the surge pile should be 1.5 cargoes, fed by a belt sized to match the plant output rate. The reclaim pit should include chute-type tunnel gates to feed the car loading belt, which will normally be of high capacity and will thus experience very few service hours per year.

At moderate volumes — to about 3,000 to 4,000 tons per hour in coal — an automatic tilt pan or pants-leg chute can be used — like those used at inside belt heads. At high volumes it will usually be found better to run the belt continuously and recycle what falls between cars into a track hopper.

A belt scale is optional. Material can be weighed out of the plant at a captive mine and a season total can be corrected for estimated inventory. A belt scale on the car loading belt will be more costly because it must be of higher capacity. (Note: recycled material must not be weighed twice.)

In general, modest-sized stations cost $50,000 to $100,000 (1966) and the most elaborate likely to arise may occasionally reach $250,000 for high rates and large trains.

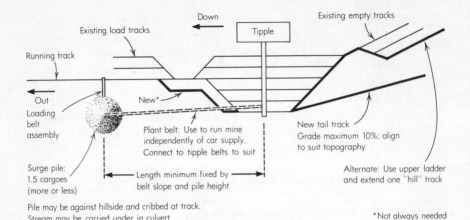

Down                    Existing empty tracks

Existing load tracks          Tipple

Running track

Out
Loading          New*
belt             Plant belt: Use to run mine        New tail track
assembly         independently of car supply.       Grade maximum 10%; align
                 Connect to tipple belts to suit    to suit topography

Surge pile:      |←— Length minimum fixed by —→|    Alternate: Use upper ladder
1.5 cargoes          belt slope and pile height     and extend one "hill" track
(more or less)

Pile may be against hillside and cribbed at track.
Stream may be carried under in culvert                        *Not always needed

### 2.1.2.1 — Coal Mine Loading Station

This installation loads on the track that serves the mine — it will be "blocked" for a few hours at a time, like it is with the mine-run train but less often. A 1,000,000 tpy operation will use this track for the integral train 80 to 200 hours a year and it will be available for conventionally handled cars the rest of the time. Usually, the easiest way to adapt to the plant is to connect the pile belt to the loading bridge at its end or to take one existing track out of service. The track parallel to the ladder is needed only if conventional-car traffic is very heavy and tipple tracks are very short. With this facility the mine can operate independently of car supply and the railroad need not serve the mine as frequently as conventional service requires. Note that no wide areas are needed — many coal mines are in narrow valleys.

## 2.1.2.2 One-Product Unloading Stations

**Power plant stations typify this type. The track hopper, sized for continuous in-motion unloading, functions as a chute to direct the material to the stacking belt. "Hopper capacity" is meaningless in the usual sense.**

The design should avoid gates or feeders — the train is the feeder. Stacking belt design is based on train time and usually will use high capacity for intermittent use and a short service life. Its drive should be on the tower. A guiding hood to stop the forward motion of the material coming off the high-speed belt is usually needed.

The cone-and-crater live surge pile should be sized for about 1.5 cargoes, contained in an earth fill or in a large "dead" storage pile of the material hauled.

A lowering chute will usually be required for dust, if not for degradation, control. An open spiral chute is recommended — telescoping chutes are more costly and contain working parts that may malfunction. Perforated towers experience jammed openings when loaded at high rates.

A high-volume station to unload 50,000-ton trains will usually cost less than $200,000 including means to dispense to the using (or reshipping) facility.

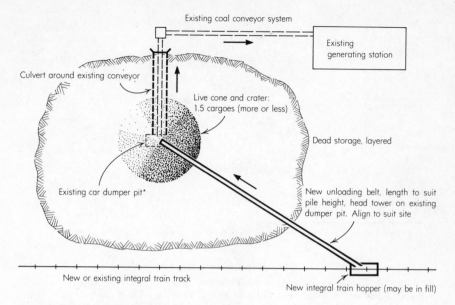

Existing coal conveyor system

Existing generating station

Culvert around existing conveyor

Live cone and crater: 1.5 cargoes (more or less)

Dead storage, layered

Existing car dumper pit*

New unloading belt, length to suit pile height, head tower on existing dumper pit. Align to suit site

New or existing integral train track

New integral train hopper (may be in fill)

*Remove dumper and accessories. Build new storage to use live crater for plant feed. Manage dead storage with dozer, direct from live cone.

### 2.1.2.2 — Power Station Modification

This sketch indicates inexpensive modifications to an existing generating station. The existing plant feed-belt system, conveniently, starts with the feeders in the dumper pit. The "dead" storage is layered into a flat-topped pile around the dumper site after removing thaw sheds, dumper and other interfering structures and installing a culvert to protect the first belt flight and provide pit access. The "live" storage will then be a cone and crater over the dumper pit. Existing systems for moving coal to dead storage can be abandoned — coal for dead storage can be moved directly to and from the "live" pile with a bulldozer.

## 2.1.2.3 Terminals Designed for Classified Storage, Blending, Etc.

In this group of stations the surge pile should contain one cargo. For unloading, the hopper and stacking belt are as for a one-commodity station, and reclaim to classified storage uses a tunnel conveyor leading to an overhead conveyor. This belt should be sized to move one cargo from the receiving cell (surge pile) to classified storage in about 80% of the interval between trains. Subsequent reclaim to the plant or dispensary is at rates governed by the consuming plant.

A station intended to load from classified storage or to load blended cargoes is similar but reversed. A cargo is put into a final loading cell in advance of train arrival and the loading belt is sized for train economy.

The design rationale is that the high-speed train-service belts should

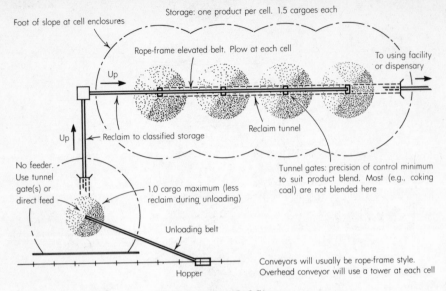

Storage: one product per cell. 1.5 cargoes each

Foot of slope at cell enclosures

Rope-frame elevated belt. Plow at each cell

To using facility or dispensary

Up

Up

Reclaim to classified storage

Reclaim tunnel

No feeder. Use tunnel gate(s) or direct feed

Tunnel gates: precision of control minimum to suit product blend. Most (e.g., coking coal) are not blended here

1.0 cargo maximum (less reclaim during unloading)

Unloading belt

Hopper

Conveyors will usually be rope-frame style. Overhead conveyor will use a tower at each cell

### 2.1.2.3-A — Classified Storage

A facility like this one will be used where several kinds of material must be received and stored separately — e.g., several kinds of coal and stone for a blast furnace plant. It contains a one-cargo transfer cell used to release the train quickly, in the interest of train economy. The distribution conveyor runs more or less continuously to pass each cargo to classified storage for further dispensing in accordance with the needs of the using plant. Such a station, properly designed, can be less costly than any scheme to "live out of the cars." The reverse, for assembly of a blended cargo in a transfer cell for shipment, should be obvious.

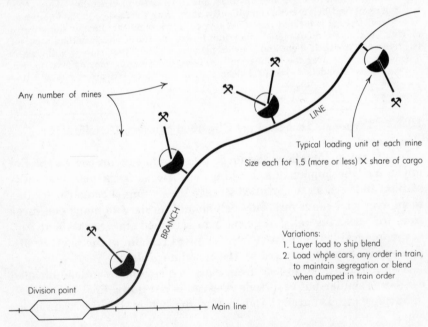

Any number of mines

LINE

Typical loading unit at each mine

Size each for 1.5 (more or less) X share of cargo

BRANCH

Variations:
1. Layer load to ship blend
2. Load whole cars, any order in train, to maintain segregation or blend when dumped in train order

Division point

Main line

### 2.1.2.3-B — Layer Loading

This illustration shows how neighboring mines can market blended coal cooperatively without rehandling coal or cars. The train can be passed by the several mines in succession. Travel and belt speed at each mine will determine how much coal each loads into the train — part-loading each car. A belt scale at each mine will report each contribution to the whole cargo.

be as short as practical to minimize cost and exposure to system malfunction that may affect the train.

Layer-loading is a variation of blended-cargo loading whereby material is put into each car from each station along a route, in turn.

### 2.1.2.4  Marine Transfer Terminals

**Stations for marine service, inbound or outbound, will differ from the typical primarily in that economics will usually dictate high-rate handling equipment on both sides of the station.**

### 2.1.2.5  Container Terminals

**Side-transferring is usually the most economic means of handling containers. A platform is used parallel to the track and the transfer unit will move containers each way between train and platform.**

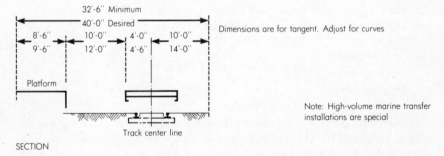

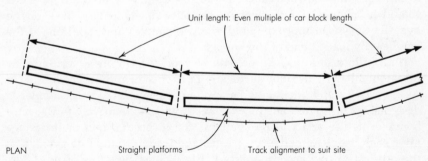

#### 2.1.2.5 — Container Terminal

Entire trains or integral car blocks are handled at once, avoiding individual cars — hence avoiding service to minor stations. A transfer unit will work more efficiently at a major point — it is a specialized trailer truck and should be kept busy. One "four-pack" (80-foot) transfer unit can handle 3,000 tons on and 3,000 tons off the train in a shift with one machine and two men.

### 2.1.2.6 Specialized Terminals

The diversity of special cases makes it impractical, by definition, to treat the possibilities exhaustively. Designers must use ingenuity; in difficult situations there is no choice but to employ an ingenious designer.

### 2.1.3 Components

Even complex terminals will use relatively few components in various combinations. Planners will find it profitable to study components individually before undertaking system or subsystem development.

#### 2.1.3.1 Unloading Hoppers

The track hopper functions as a chute to direct material to the belt. Its design starts with an estimate of its length. The variables are unloading train speed, car clearing time, and load density.

For example: Hypothecate an unloading rate of 15,000 tph, load density of 1.8 tons per foot of train and an individual car-clearing time of 40 seconds, including time to open the doors. Speed is:

$$\frac{15,000}{1.8 \times 3,600} = 2.5 \text{ feet per second (approx.)}$$

Hopper length is:

$$2.5 \times 40 = 100 \text{ feet}$$

It is seldom practical to provide the depth needed for a gravity hopper of this length. Therefore the hopper sketched uses a belt to move material from the "downstream" end to the deep part of the hopper. It should be planned for an average capacity of about 25%-30% of the overall (4,000 tph, approximately, in the example) and should be at the less heavily loaded end of the hopper.

Hopper interiors may be of poured concrete, gunite or cribbing or of earth fill with flexible surfacing (e.g., penetration macadam). In special cases metal liners may be applied. In general, a track hopper is designed for minimum adequacy, since it will see relatively few service hours in its life and will be available for inspection and maintenance after each trainload delivery. (Gates and feeders should be avoided in the interest of cost and reliability.) Rigid construction is of no differential value at the characteristic low train speeds; hence cribbing and fill, not framed construction, will be usual.

When makeshift or modified conventional cross-hopper cars are used it will seldom be advantageous to plan bridge-type hopper tops to accommodate material spilled outside the rails. Most such material (especially coal) can be diverted over the top of the rail to the opening. New cars of new design will dump between the rails.

When laying out integral train track hoppers, steep grades can be used for short distances. A grade of 8% for 200 to 400 feet (to gain as much as 30 feet above existing grade) is easily accommodated in most installations. (Ground water, difficult digging, minimizing stacking conveyor length or other considerations favor the use of above-ground installations.)

Designers should plan for fillets, smooth flow, large openings and generous belt capacity so that the hopper will actually be a chute. Continuous flow to the pile is important.

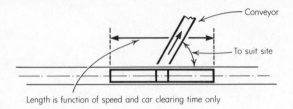

To suit site

See 2.1.3.1-B for alternate to suit converted coal cars

Length is function of speed and car clearing time only

Note: Design should be cognizant of **few** hours' use during service life

PLAN

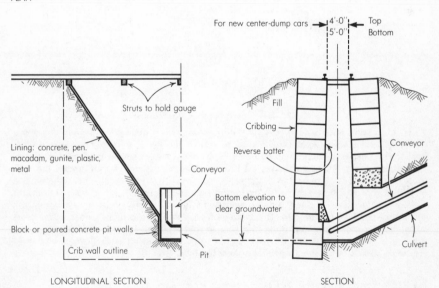

**2.1.3.1-A — Track Hopper General Arrangement**

A low-cost track hopper can be built with cribbed walls, thus avoiding costly foundations — if the track becomes a bit wavy, it is still usable at 1 or 2 miles per hour while unloading. Such a hopper is easily adaptable to diverse environments because the steel, concrete or improvised cribbing is simple to build and modify. The conveyor tail pit should be structurally independent of the crib walls above — lintels should be used to isolate it. Hopper sidewalls should be battered inward to prevent material hang-up, and top struts will hold track gauge.

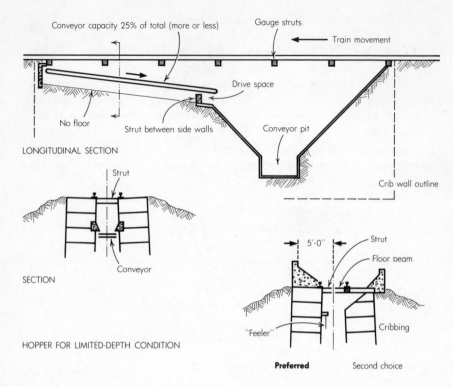

Conveyor capacity 25% of total (more or less)

Gauge struts

← Train movement

Drive space

No floor

Strut between side walls

Conveyor pit

LONGITUDINAL SECTION

Crib wall outline

Strut

Conveyor

SECTION

HOPPER FOR LIMITED-DEPTH CONDITION

5'-0"

Strut

Floor beam

"Feeler"

Cribbing

**Preferred**    Second choice

TOP TREATMENT FOR CONVERTED COAL CARS

Generally applicable

### 2.1.3.1-B — Track Hopper Variations

When high train speeds require a long hopper or where high groundwater dictates a shallow hopper, a conveyor can be used to return the last-discharged elements of the load to the hopper. When modified cross-hopper coal cars must be used, material falling outside the track can be diverted into the hopper either over or under the rail. Most materials can be passed over the rail — e.g., coal that will crush under the wheels or pellets that will flow easily. An exception would be found in large stone that might cause derailments. A "feeler" may be wanted to detect overfill — e.g., a stoppage of the conveyor — and signal or stop the train before disastrous pileups occur. The most suitable style uses a pendant hung in a ring so that a circuit is shorted when the hanging rod is displaced. Undue reliance should not be placed on such devices — at most economic speeds they give a warning almost too late.

## 2.1.3.2   Train Service Belts

Belts used to load and unload the trains should usually be of high capacity; their size will derive from train-time economics. They should usually be of rope-frame design, with clear-span "suspension bridge" support — for economy. Separate walkways are not needed for the limited maintenance expected during their relatively few hours of intermittent service. Prelubricated bearings, overloaded motors and light belts can be used.

For example, a 5,000-tph belt at a 1,000,000-tpy power plant will see only 2,000 service hours in 10 years — equivalent of less than 3 months of full-time use. It will be available for inspection if needed after each few hours of use.

Capacities can be derived by extrapolating speed from commercial conveyor capacity tables. Speeds up to 1,200 to 1,300 fpm are usually economic.

The design of such components is essentially an exercise in costing. The designer should estimate the annual reduction in train time cost obtainable from successive increments of belt width and speed and then estimate incremental cost of each increment of belt width and speed. The investment in each increment of belt and speed can then be compared to the annual saving in train time. Belt operating cost and longevity seldom affect the comparison, since economic utilizations of train service belts are usually low. Since train time is costly, the widest readily available belt, run as fast as possible, will usually be a sound investment.

Train service belts should often be dualized to save train time when economy seems to call for unavailable capacities. For example:

Hypothecate 4,000,000 tons of coal annually when the largest individual belt capacity available for the project is 7,000 tph. Train time is worth $9.00 per minute and stacking belts must be 700 feet long.

With one belt the station will use

$$\frac{4,000,000}{7,000} = 572 \text{ hr per year train time.}$$

With two belts the station will use

$$\frac{4,000,000}{14,000} = 286 \text{ hr per year;}$$

annual train time saving is

$$572 - 286 = 286 \text{ hr per year.}$$

This train time saving is worth

$$286 \times 60 \times 9 = \$157,000 \text{ per year.}$$

At an IATI rate of 20% this annual saving will support

$$\frac{157,000}{0.20} = \$785,000.$$

The second belt (sharing hopper and part, at least, of the structure) will cost considerably less than this sum. Before choosing a design the planner should make a similar comparison for three, four or more belts until an increment is found that will cost more than it is worth. Designers must not be diverted from their economic objectives by the fact that the belts will be lightly used.

## 2.1.3.4  Transfer Cells

A transfer cell is a specialized storage unit.  Its function is to receive a cargo from the train quickly (to permit the train to depart) for subsequent transfer to storage or other use (or to receive a cargo from classified storage or blending for shipment).  Its use permits minimizing the length of high-capacity train-service belt and minimizes the risk of train delay due to belt breakdown.

It will require smaller capacity than a cell which must *also* accommodate schedule irregularity.  (Usually it is sized for exactly one cargo.) It will often handle varying kinds of cargo in succession and hence must be lined with more attention to clean unloading than would a cell handling the same material every trip.

Its sizing is simply a matter of geometry.

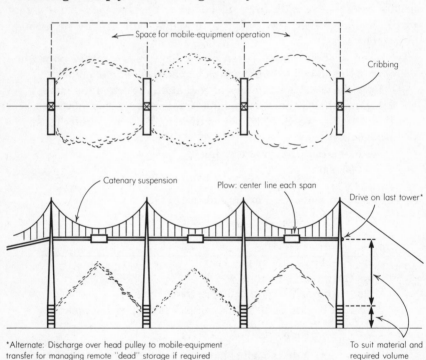

*Alternate: Discharge over head pulley to mobile-equipment
transfer for managing remote "dead" storage if required

To suit material and
required volume

### 2.1.3.5-A — Classified Storage for Sticky Material

Materials that will not flow readily into a conveyor tunnel are best handled with mobile equipment.  In such cases the distribution conveyor can be elevated on low-cost rope-frame construction with the towers between piles, protected by cribbing. The belt can be discharged at the center of any span by using a plow — the rope-frame support is not rigid enough for a tripper to function satisfactorily, and rigid bridges are unwarrantedly costly.  The mobile equipment used can be self-loading scrapers ("pans") if desired, but most applications will be better served by front-end loaders which can be had in sizes up to 35 tons.

## 2.1.3.5  Distribution Conveyors and Classified Storage

Distribution conveyors will ordinarily run from a transfer cell to a series of classified cells. There will be two classes of such installations:
  A — Installations designed for mobile equipment reclaim,
  B — Installations designed for tunnel reclaim.
The first will be used for low volume and for which low-rate or intermittent reclaim is difficult — e.g., natural iron ore. The second will be used when free-flowing materials are handled in enough volume to warrant the use of a reclaim tunnel.

At stations designed for mobile equipment reclaim, the distribution conveyor is best designed in rope-frame belt, supported on towers located between piles, out of the way of mobile equipment. Each discharge then must be located at midspan where trippers are unduly costly — hence plows.

At stations designed for tunnel reclaim, cell spacing is about equal to the diameter of the "live" cone, with supports at the center of each cell.

Roof (if needed) alternates:
  1) Radial inclined cables and standard deck, each cell.
  2) Quonset-type covering all; conveyor suspended from roof at highest point. Span equal to diameter of "live" cones

Plow (or tripper) at each intermediate tower.
Spiral chutes if needed

Drive at last tower

Fill

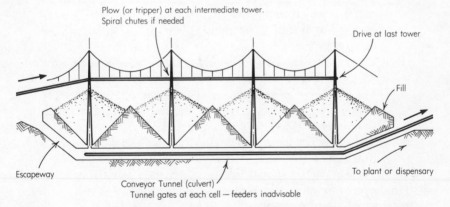

Escapeway

Conveyor Tunnel (culvert)
Tunnel gates at each cell — feeders inadvisable

To plant or dispensary

#### 2.1.3.5-B — Classified Storage for Tunnel Reclaim

When materials can be relied on to flow into a conveyor tunnel (sometimes with a rapper on the gate hopper), mobile equipment need not be used. In such cases the tower for each span can be supported on the reclaim pit. A plow or fixed tripper can be used, with or without spiral chute, at each cell. Cells themselves should usually be made up of fill with flexible lining, or they can be lined with the product to minimize first cost and maintenance. Gates to the reclaim belt should be simple tunnel gates, avoiding mechanical feeders for simplicity, cost and reliability. The headroom needed for chute-gates instead of clamshells will usually be a good investment in terms of reliability. The tunnel itself can be of flexible culvert pipe — and one aggregate producer successfully uses junked tank car bodies for a low-cost reclaim tunnel.

Plows or trippers can be used, at the designer's option. When trippers are used they will be fixed, using only a simple in-chute flop gate.

Distribution conveyors should be designed to empty the transfer cell in 80% of the interval between trains, using high-speed, lightweight belts. This design criterion will usually yield considerable time for inspection and service when the belt is not in use. Therefore walkways and rigid galleries are not needed.

### 2.1.3.6  Trippers and Plows

When distribution conveyors are planned for tunnel reclaim, a plow or tripper can be installed atop each tower. When the belt must be unloaded in midspan on a rope-frame conveyor there is little choice but to use a retractable plow. This hardware is not commercially available — vendors preferring to sell the more costly trippers and associated costly longevity-design conveyors and conveyor bridges. Therefore it must be designed for each installation, more or less according to the accompanying sketch. It is seldom, if ever, economic to use a traveling tripper or its equivalent. (One exception is an application of a traveling plow to trimming a self-loading high-capability ship.)

Traveling devices or midspan trippers have these disadvantages, all economic:

A — They require costly bridges which, in turn, require foundations which can prevent settlement (the rope-frame conveying system is structurally immune to settlement damage).

B — They require heavier belts and drives to accommodate the required belt tension.

C — They involve degradation exposure at all intermediate trippers that are not in use for any delivery and at which the material is avoidably transferred.

D — They involve more working parts and exposure to malfunction.

The retractable plow shown in the sketch is a very simple device, though design may be modified to each application if desired.

Its principal components are:

A — A fixed, two-sided plow supported to clear the material on the carrying run under normal conditions.

B — A stainless-clad plate under the carrying run of the belt capable of being raised to bring the belt into contact with the plow.

In use the flat plate is raised to bring the belt to plowing position before the flow of material is started; all material on the belt will then be plowed off at the applied plow. The force applied to the plow by the moving material will be transmitted into the supporting cables, with the torque about a transverse axis producing a differential tension between the catenary and the sideframe cables.

The flat plate will be lifted to plowing position and held there (usually) by hydraulic pressure. The hydraulic system will be a self-contained circuit installed on the assembly, electrically remote-controlled. The system will be under pressure only when the plow is in use and the pump is running, returning by gravity to disengaged position when the pump is stopped.

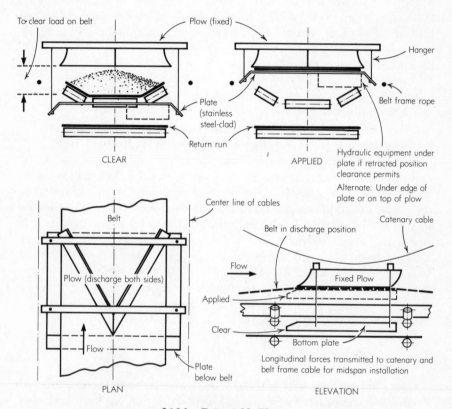

### 2.1.3.6 — Retractable Plow

This plow is intended for intermittent use. Designers should reflect on the actual number of service hours an individual plow will be used during its amortization period. It is intended for low-budget design and is not sold at this writing as a complete "package" by any vendor. Its construction is within the capability of the hydraulic machine mechanic at a coal mine or similar installation.

The bottom plate should be of stainless or stainless-clad steel to minimize belt wear. The plow leading edges should be finished with belting material to plow the belt clear. The hydraulic pump and its motor should be of such dimensions and/or location (e.g., under the edges, clear of the return belt) as will avoid interference when the plate is lowered. The assembly should be secured to both pairs of longitudinal ropes and a set of vertical guides should be provided to transmit the drag from the plate to the cables. It must, in most rope-frame, catenary installations, be located at a support or midspan.

### 2.1.3.7 Mobile Reclaim

Sticky materials or other materials that are difficult to handle in chutes or which tend to rathole are best reclaimed by using mobile equipment. Such tools include front-end loaders (available in 1967 up to 35-ton size), self-loading scrapers ("pans"), and other devices from the construction trade.

In general, reclaim for consumption will be relatively slow, hence using small chutes, gates and conveyors. Attempts to develop fully automatic systems for such uses usually lead to very high costs. Tunnel feeders, scrapers and the like are assiduously promoted by vendors but cost-oriented planners will usually resort to mobile tools in such cases.

### 2.1.3.8 Mobile Loading

At many shipping stations where either
   A — volume is low or
   B — the material is difficult to handle by gravity and conveyor,
it will be advantageous to use mobile equipment to load the train.

In such applications large (35-ton) front-end loaders will usually be best suited. In such stations the surge pile must be accumulated near the track by a stacking belt sized to suit the plant and running when the plant runs; pile size should be about 1.5 cargoes. The mobile loader will be used to distribute the material conveniently along the track in advance of arrival of the train.

The large front-end loaders can handle payloads of the order of 30 tons and can load about 15 cars (nominal 100's) per hour per machine. It is advisable to size the loader bucket to an even fraction of actual car capacity for the material involved. In this way there is no danger of overloading and little spillage.

### 2.1.3.9 Containers

Container systems will ordinarily use standard containers, with standard side-transfer trucks for which no special treatment here is needed.

### 2.1.4 General Arrangements

Arrangements are largely matters of ingenuity, given understanding of systems, functions and components. The constraints are seldom as restrictive as they at first appear. This section is not a complete catalog —— there can be none. It is intended to suggest adaptations to ingenious readers.

In nearly all cases various refinements will be proposed and should be subject to economic analysis. The only important source of money for such justifications will usually be train time savings, except where train crews are paid an arbitrary for changing ends. Such justifications will obviously depend on frequency, attainable time savings and train time value. The computation is essentially the same as that made for a dual train service belt, above. Planners must resist and demand substantiation for all claims that exit switches or other refinements are "operationally necessary" — they seldom are. They often are a convenience but planners must be adamant about economic justification of

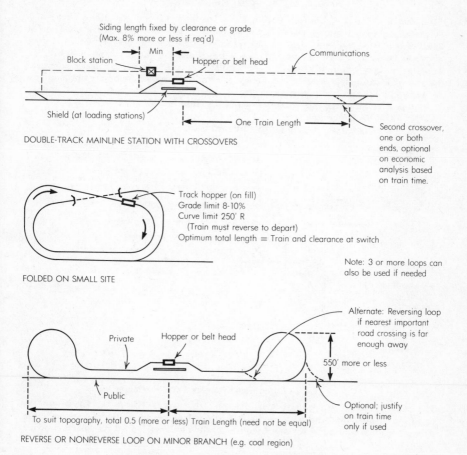

Siding length fixed by clearance or grade
(Max. 8% more or less if req'd)

Block station — Min — Hopper or belt head — Communications

Shield (at loading stations)

One Train Length

DOUBLE-TRACK MAINLINE STATION WITH CROSSOVERS

Second crossover, one or both ends, optional on economic analysis based on train time.

Track hopper (on fill)
Grade limit 8-10%
Curve limit 250' R
(Train must reverse to depart)
Optimum total length = Train and clearance at switch

Note: 3 or more loops can also be used if needed

FOLDED ON SMALL SITE

Alternate: Reversing loop if nearest important road crossing is far enough away

Private     Hopper or belt head

550' more or less

Public

Optional; justify on train time only if used

To suit topography, total 0.5 (more or less) Train Length (need not be equal)

REVERSE OR NONREVERSE LOOP ON MINOR BRANCH (e.g. coal region)

### 2.1.4-A — Station General Arrangements

This sketch will illustrate the point that designers' ingenuity is about the only limitation on types of station track arrangement. Equipment can be had or built to negotiate curves of 250-foot radius, though extremely short radii are not desirable. Similarly, steep, short grades can be used freely for integral trains. It should always be noted that station track is used intermittently and at low speeds, so it need not be of costly construction.

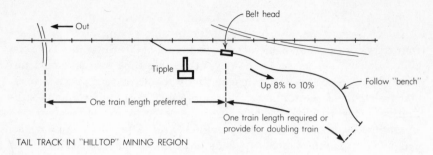

TAIL TRACK IN "HILLTOP" MINING REGION

### 2.1.4-B — Coal Mine Station

This sketch shows a specialized station for a frequently found coal mine situation — where topography requires, as it often does in coal, that the station be located at the head of a narrow valley where the tail track can be extended only by using a steep grade to be used only by the empty train — the train loads as it moves downhill. Its superior braking system allows it to be controlled on such a grade, especially when the loads are all on the less severe grade below the tipple. If a train length is not available to the next public crossing the choices are:

A — Block the crossing while the *rest* of the train loads.
B — Cut for the crossing.
C — Eliminate the crossing for the integral train.

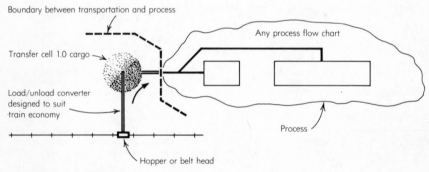

GENERALIZED FLOW CHART

### 2.1.4-C — Generalized Process Plant Station

The sketch shows a generalized flow diagram. The first belt from the track — or last belt to the train — and the associated surge pile belong conceptually to transportation. Any other plant flow chart for any function at all is independent of transportation.

even innocuous-seeming small refinements lest their accumulation carry total budgets to unacceptable levels.

*For example:* If a train will need 5.0 hr to load and there is only 0.85 train length to the nearest crossing, the crossing will be blocked (in the absence of other measures) for $0.15 \times 5.0 = 0.75$ hr or 45 minutes. Decisions on crossing treatment are

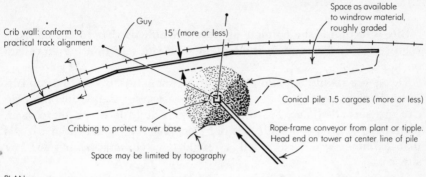

Crib wall: conform to practical track alignment

Guy

15' (more or less)

Space as available to windrow material, roughly graded

Conical pile 1.5 cargoes (more or less)

Cribbing to protect tower base

Rope-frame conveyor from plant or tipple. Head end on tower at center line of pile

Space may be limited by topography

PLAN

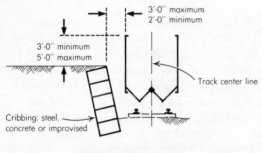

3'-0" maximum
2'-0" minimum

3'-0" minimum
5'-0" maximum

Track center line

Cribbing: steel, concrete or improvised

SECTION

### 2.1.4-D — Station for Mobile Equipment Loading

This station is for use in materials that will not flow readily or where other considerations prevent the use of gravity and belt stations. For example, a group of neighboring low-volume stations might share the cost of a large front-end loader. Very cramped space might prevent the use of the cone-and-crater pile whose total volume theoretically is four times the live volume. It is desirable to size the loader to load a car in a whole number of scoops, whether the car is loaded to weight or volume, to prevent overloading the car. This consideration, itself, can justify mobile equipment when loading a high-cube car with dense material in part of a composite cycle.

based on 45 minutes, not 5 hours of occupancy each time the train arrives, which may be at intervals of several days or weeks. Such discussions will usually involve highly generalized, sometimes emotional lectures on occupancy, "constant" use, etc.

*For example:* In a steel mill there will be extemporaneous remarks about how "everything" must stop when a long train approaches. In fact, planners must make detailed occupancy studies for *each* critical location within such a plant and objectively evaluate all available alternatives in economic terms — most "constantly used" tracks are, in fact, used only occasionally.

## 2.1.5 Site Selection

Site selection is the epitome of "local" problems. There are no fixed requirements. The system is adaptable and site selection therefore can be flexible.

Designers should not allow divided responsibility to lead to establishment of rigid requirements — so many acres, so deep a lot, etc. He can use second-choice, low-cost sites, often at little or no increase in plant cost. It is advisable to consider steep, narrow, or irregular parcels that are otherwise hard to sell, to exploit system adaptability for low site cost.

A treatment of the problem of site selection can at best be a partial catalog of ingenious treatments of specific cases. Examples can be noted thus:

A site between a highway and a railroad where narrow parcels are unsalable. Such a site can be used for either a container terminal or for some parts of a bulk terminal.

A steep site where the gravity flow can be downhill and other kinds of industrial building are difficult.

A restricted site where the surge pile can be contained in cribbing to avoid costly demolition of neighboring facilities or acquisition of land. Variants arise where streams, tracks and roads are carried through the earth fill in culvert pipe.

A conversion project where the optimum site for the new surge pile is often at an existing car dumper — where the existing user plant conveyor system begins.

In general, the tone should be one of caution to avoid prejudgement. Fitting into a difficult site is usually easier than inexperienced integral train system designers will expect.

*For example:* In the narrow valleys of the coal region the problem of finding a terminal site is admittedly difficult. However, most cases can be dealt with in either of two ways:

Use a tail track up to the "bench" that is found in most coal regions at an outcrop line. The tail track can use heavy grades because only the empty train runs uphill — with the same power the loaded train uses.

Use a tight loop, with radii of 300 feet or less. If even this curvature forces serious cutting into the hillsides (taking advantage of creek junctions and other valley openings), then a nonreversing loop should be used to permit heavy grades. Sidehill surge piles over a culvert-enclosed stream are acceptable, or even over a culvert-enclosed track using roof gates to load.

## 2.1.6 Accessories

**Accessories for oft-recurring needs will suggest applications for designers' ingenuity. "Far out" research is seldom needed but a wide knowledge of available industrial components will help — as will some comprehension of uses their designers and vendors did not anticipate.**

A few situations can be reviewed here — the nature of the problem attaches importance to ingenuity, and no catalog could be complete. The emphasis is on simple, not on elaborate or sophisticated, gadgets.

The most often required accessory will be grade crossing elimination, usually on minor roads. In planning such facilities, the capability of the

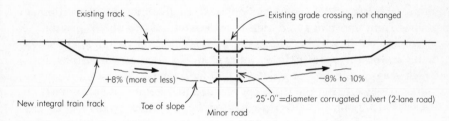

For secondary road

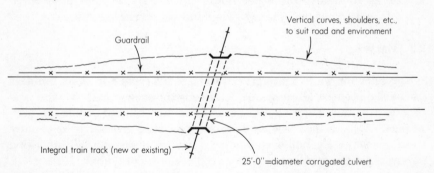

For primary road

### 2.1.6 — Highway Crossing Eliminations

The use of corrugated steel culvert pipe offers a low-cost way to eliminate public road crossings — e.g., within the working length of a train at a terminal. A secondary road can be carried through a large metal pipe without disturbing the grade of the running track or of the road. In that situation the integral train operates on what amounts to a siding with a steep profile over the culvert, on grades a conventional train could not negotiate. The existing through track can be left unchanged for other traffic. This construction can reflect a low level of utilization and low speeds. Alternatively a road can be carried over a track. This arrangement is usually best for important roads. The road profile, geometric features, shoulders, etc., should reflect the nature of the road — "freeway" standards would be inappropriate on a town street. Similarly, uncontrolled fill would be adequate for the siding but inadequate for a major highway.

integral train should be exploited fully, and this application can thus illustrate a basic design "philosophy" which applies generally.

When the integral train is to use an existing track whose grade is not to be changed, the integral train's overpass can be built on a siding, leaving the existing grade crossing undisturbed for main-track traffic. In some cases the embankment can be used as a site for an unloading or recycling hopper that will then be free of ground water problems.

In most cases integral train grade separations will use culvert pipe tunnels, commercially available in diameters up to 25 feet. Such pipe is nearly always less costly than a framed structure and is adequate for the needs — to carry either a track, a secondary public road, or an industrial access road.

In other structure situations, retaining walls will be needed. In most cases cribbing will be used — usually steel bin-walls but sometimes concrete cribbing. Such construction is virtually immune to settlement damage and thus can avoid high-cost foundations in difficult ground.

Sometimes it will be necessary or desirable to weigh loads where belts scales are unsuitable or unwanted. In such cases, an electronic track scale weighing one axle at a time will usually be found most economical — weighing the train both loaded and empty and automatically (electronically or digitally) integrating the net. Such scales will employ weigh rails about 5 feet long and can be used at loading or unloading speeds up to about 1 mile per hour. Such systems yield total cargo weights and do not undertake to yield individual car weights.

## 2.2 Cars

Car selection and/or design criteria are all economic. Car builders obviously propose all-new cars, and sometimes new cars *are* the best choice. But the choice should be made on an economic basis for each project. A claim that new cars are an "operating necessity" is usually unsupportable. Economic comparisons can be made only by estimating *all* variables for each case. A few guides can be provided:

A — It is rarely economic to use new cars of presently available design. Railway car design has not progressed and a new car has little advantage except longer prospective life. The "extra" investment will seldom yield any return in a commercially realistic 10-to-12-year capital recovery period.

B — If service conditions and traffic demand permit high speeds (averages of upwards of 50 mph) and/or very large trains (25,000 tons net and up), then the case for new cars (of new design) is probably robust.

C — If the capital recovery period must be longer than about 10
years to justify new equipment, the case is probably weak.

D — If allocated costs must be used to support new cars — e.g.,
the traditional "big cars, hence few cars" pitch — then the
case for new cars is probably weak.

Economy usually demands special cars — sometimes just to make
them special and control their use if it comes to that, but it seldom will.
Sealed bearings, dual air lines, insulation and heat, appropriate door
hardware, solid drawbars, unit brakes, and elimination of avoidable
parts can usually reduce first cost, maintenance cost and tare weight.
Simplification, per se, is usually economic because of the economic effect of reduced delay and repair time allowances.

Reliability is essential — delay allowances normally cost more than
reliable cars. More reliable cars do not necessarily cost more than conventional cars. Most conventional railway gear is unreliable in terms of
mission-completion — new cars of present designs almost as seriously
so as older cars of essentially the same design. As is often the case in
engineering matters, it is detail parts that contribute most of the problems.

Tare weight becomes economically vital as utilizations improve. As a
rule of thumb, 1 pound of tare weight *reduction* in a bulk train will support $1 in car investment at often-encountered relationships (300 mi/
day, 2.5 mills/t.m. freight rate, 10-year amortization, 6% interest, 50%
empty).

## 2.2.1 Reliability and Availability

**Pragmatically considered, reliability is related to availability. Road
failures cost (directly and indirectly) so much that preventive maintenance is economically mandatory. This is also true of conventional
railroading, but nondefinitive cost concepts obscure the fact and inhibit
improvements. It follows that suitable design can convert reliability
into availability by reducing out-of-service time (including delay allowances). Designers will find that the quantitative concept of reliability,
as it is known in other trades, is unknown among railway suppliers.**

Integral train cars live relatively sheltered lives — e.g., no humping,
no "bonfire" thawing, no sledgehammer door operation. But the cars
will develop considerable mileage — often 250,000 to 300,000 miles per
year for a 10-year service life.

*For example:* One round trip from northern Minnesota to
Pittsburgh (800 miles each way) for a 40,000-ton train of 100-
ton cars involves about

$$400 \times 800 \times 2 = 640,000 \text{ car miles.}$$

Conventional bearings would produce one hotbox every two or three trips — from just one kind of failure.

Clearly, if each such mission is to be completed reliably, the matter demands close attention. The *train* is the planning unit, and a road set-off delays the whole train. Design experience thus far indicates that the following are minima:

A — Closed bearings (cartridge or roller)

B — Replacement of as many as possible of the couplers and draft gear with solid drawbars and associated fixed air connections

C — Composition brake shoes

D — Replacement of door hardware with, at least, the Enterprise type "D" which permits opening and closing with a car wrench

E — Use of insulation and heat to prevent freezing

F — For long trains a second air line which will maintain air tanks independently of the train pipe

G — Steel wheels

The cars must be operated so that they are rotated out of service, usually in blocks, periodically. Practical schedules are:

*For modified conventional (new or secondhand) cars.* Rotate each car out on a quarterly basis for detailed shop attention. Inspect and perform minor routine service at least monthly. Inspect after every round trip.

*For newly designed cars of sophisticated design:* Rotate each car out on a semiannual basis for detailed shop attention. Inspect and perform minor routine service bi-monthly or quarterly. Inspect after every trip.

Scheduling realities require that a car be rotated for one whole interval or train cycle. In general, modified secondhand cars will require at least twice as much time for periodic in-train attention as newly designed cars.

Newly designed cars can be expected to run for about 12 years — 3,500,000 to 4,000,000 miles. This figure is not subject to nor capable of objective proof at this stage, but it appears to be attainable. It is not likely that modified existing cars can approach this service life; 1,500,000 to 2,000,000 miles is optimistic. Such cars will be economic where modest use density is expected — about 100,000 to 150,000 miles per year with a projected life of 10 years and a "spare ratio" of about 10% — i.e., provide about 1 spare for every 10 cars needed in service. Even then, such makeshift operations may often depend on better utilization as experience is gained to make the fleet last out a 10-year service life, after some individual cars have been retired.

In using newly designed cars it will be advisable to increase the fleet size 1 to 2 percent for switching out car blocks found defective out of turn on inspection. When using modified secondhand cars this allowance should be about 5 percent. These figures, too, are incapable of objective computation, and further research may be warranted. Past railroad experience is not entirely relevant.

All integral train systems are designed to avoid such abuse as external thawing or the use of clamshells to unload bulk. Strict adherence to the anticipated service conditions is necessary to attain the desired reliability.

## 2.2.2 Modified Cars

As long as railroads persist in conventional low-utilization operations there will be a surplus of secondhand cars. Such cars are often inappropriate for unrestricted service but can be used for the "sheltered life" of an integral train car. Car design has not progressed appreciably, and new cars essentially of existing designs cannot often be justified. The "modification package" for a new car is substantially the same as for a rescued junker.

*For example:* A salesman for a contemporary earthmover can claim his machine will do work that a 10-year-old machine could not do when it was new. A coal car salesman cannot so claim.

The modifications needed for existing cars — new or old — include the following:

A — Replace cast-iron with steel wheels, cast or wrought.

B — Replace open bearings with cartridge or roller bearings.

C — Replace door hardware (in bulk service) with Enterprise type "D" hardware (without locking dogs) (or similar) to eliminate door abuse.

D — Remove conventional brake rigging, either at the outset or as replacements or major repairs are needed, and use truck-mounted, on-tread unit brake systems.

E — Apply spray-on urethane insulation if the car is to be used in northern climates in bulk services.

F — Apply car heat (see section 2.2.5) if the car is to be used in northern climates in bulk services. This precaution is recommended even when handling such materials as pellets that theoretically should not freeze.

G — Modify the car body by removing all surplus metal (there is considerable in the form of roof plates, door hardware, draft gear, and the like) and, if appropriate, sideboard or cut down cars to suit the commodity hauled.

H — Remove up to 80% to 90% of center sill extensions and

draft gear, replacing with solid drawbars, either at the outset or in lieu of repairs. Replace separable air hose with solid, one-piece hose connections.

Cars must be selected on an individual basis. It will often be advisable to "cannibalize" from a "junker" fleet to assemble acceptable cars.

### 2.2.3 New Cars

This section reviews basic new car types for bulk and container service. They can be had without awaiting major breakthroughs, and should not be regarded as "ultimates." When proposing new cars, economy demands design improvements. Once the idea of a new design is accepted, basic improvements are economically imperative. The resistance that will be encountered is to the idea that there *can* be an improvement in car design.

The sketches show general arrangements only. Such cars should be designed for the service, from the beginning. The car body, trucks,

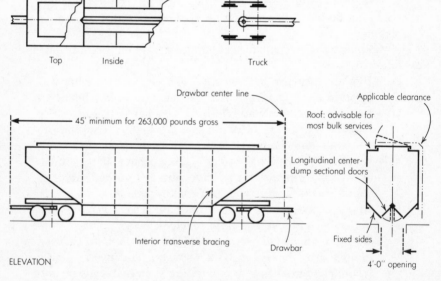

Top        Inside                    Truck

ELEVATION

Drawbar center line

|← 45' minimum for 263,000 pounds gross →|

Applicable clearance

Roof: advisable for most bulk services

Longitudinal center-dump sectional doors

Interior transverse bracing

Drawbar

Fixed sides

4'-0" opening

#### 2.2.3-A — Bulk Car

This sketch illustrates some vital characteristics of a next-generation bulk car for integral train service. The straight sides, between-rails dumping and solid-drawbar truck-center articulation are fundamental and readily available improvements. The gates should be closed by air and held with spring-loaded latches, released by applying air to pull them. Over-center, sliding and drive-open types are rarely optimum. Material should be alloy steel until and unless light-metal vendors can make a convincing case.

brakes, etc., are all new but not "novel." The sketches are not intended to represent ultimates — no ultimate is likely ever to emerge. Nor can the sketches include details — advancing technology will obsolete details quickly anyway.

It is expected that the bulk car, sized for coal, can be readily brought to a tare weight of about 40,000 to 45,000 pounds (of an allowed 263,000 total). It is expected that an 80-foot container car can be held to about 40,000 to 45,000 pounds, allowing four 20-foot (maximum 20-ton) containers within the rail loading of a nominal 70-ton car. A 70-ton (nominal) bulk car will be needed for some services where low-capacity railroad must be used (e.g., Canadian wheat).

Car doors for new bulk cars should be controlled either by an automatic (electronic) or manual (pushbutton) system. In either case air is admitted to the cylinder that opens the latch when the car comes over the hopper and to the cylinder that closes the door after it leaves the hopper. In either case a locked control in the train cab makes the entire door system inoperative until it is unlocked at the delivery terminal.

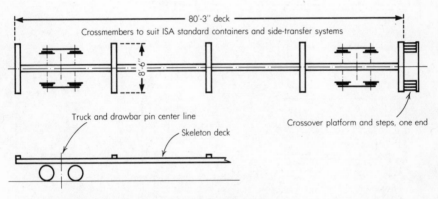

**2.2.3-B — Container Car**

The car shown can accommodate four standard 20-foot containers or equivalent. It should be skeletonized, with a crossover walkway at one end. Units should be articulated in blocks with solid drawbars pinned at truck centers, with couplers only at block ends. The cars will be narrow — highway limits will govern the containers — and the long truck center distance thus will not pose the problem it would for a wide car.

## 2.2.4 Special Cars

**The two examples in this section illustrate the two major kinds of cases — low-budget modified cars and newly designed cars. Designers will need ingenuity since each case is, by definition, special.**

Special car design is limited only by designers' ingenuity. The garbage cars are shown not because hauling garbage is likely to be a major source of revenue (though it *is* a growth industry) but to indicate forcefully, in an unlikely area, that ingenuity has a vital place. This car is a low-budget modification based on using what is almost junk as far as any other use is concerned. Such cars would be used in blocks but are unlikely to be self-powered.

The lumber car is essentially the one developed by a major car builder (Pullman), with modifications for integral train service. In integral train use it would be applied to lumber and other trades, in the form of captive car blocks with or without power in the blocks. Combining sophisticated power and makeshift cars is unlikely to be economically sound. (Contemporary diesels are *not* sophisticated power.)

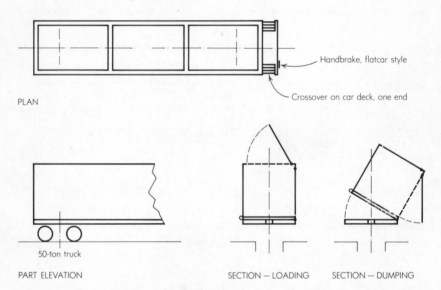

PLAN

Handbrake, flatcar style

Crossover on car deck, one end

50-ton truck

PART ELEVATION          SECTION — LOADING    SECTION — DUMPING

#### 2.2.4-A — Garbage Car

A car for light-loading material such as refuse must be improvised — there is no "ready-made" design extant. The body should be designed with a swinging lid — in sections with torsion bars — and one top-hung side. The basic car can be a second-hand stockcar, gondola, or similar 50-ton obsolete unit. The car can be dumped by using a hook adapter on a 35-ton front-end loader to lift the side opposite the opening. The lifting bar can be incorporated into a door latch by using a bar across the car under the floor so that applying a lifting force will unlatch the door. The floor should be made of scrap rails to receive heavy objects but otherwise the car body can use very light framing for "balloon" freight. This car is sketched to indicate the use of ingenuity in using what is at hand to earn a profit from even such an unpromising trade as garbage-hauling — for which, incidentally, the usual open cars and slow-motion operations are not acceptable at any price.

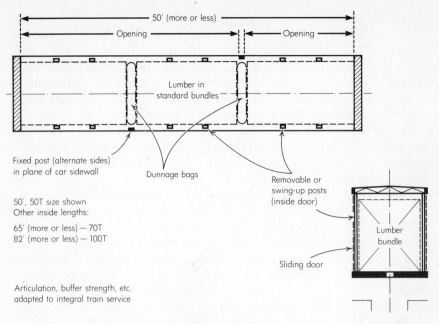

50' (more or less)

Opening — Opening

Lumber in standard bundles

Fixed post (alternate sides) in plane of car sidewall

Dunnage bags

Removable or swing-up posts (inside door)

50', 50T size shown
Other inside lengths:

65' (more or less) — 70T
82' (more or less) — 100T

Lumber bundle

Sliding door

Articulation, buffer strength, etc. adapted to integral train service

### 2.2.4-B — Lumber Car

This car is essentially a bulkhead flat with a shelter, using light doors and removable or swing-away posts to prevent side-shifting of the load. Bundles can be unitized in standard configurations for fast loading (about 15 minutes for a 70-ton car). A train can visit several sawmills in a day and gather considerable cargo without needing a separate spot-and-pick-up function. The car can be used in blocks for wallboard, bagged or cartoned unitized loads, etc.

## 2.2.5 Car Heat

**Even if bulk freight is loaded dry, rain and snow in cold weather can cause freezing. In theory all that is needed is insulation, but an insulated, unheated car, if delayed, can freeze and then cannot be thawed. At the present "state of the art" low-budget heat can be considered low-cost insurance against the unforeseen. It is advisable to heat even covered cars — the lading can be wet.**

The most practical and economic form of car heat for bulk freight is electric resistance heat. Heat must be applied over the entire surface of the car body, including doors (except tops) and no simple commercially available heater, at any price (at this writing) will do the job adequately. Hence the present recommendations. Insulation should be applied to the whole car body, including roof, doors, hatches, sides, slopes, etc.

Some computer runs have predicted and field observations tend to verify that car-body heat is primarily a preventive measure — theoretically not needed. It appears that most requirements will be met if about 7.5 kw are applied to a hopper car body of 70- to 100-ton size, open or covered. The objective is to maintain the metal at about 35 degrees F. when the car is loaded. The lading itself is an insulator on the inside of the car. Covered cars will not accumulate snow and will avoid outdoor exposure of body inner surfaces when empty. Open cars in snow country may present marginal conditions on occasion.

The most practical arrangement thus far devised is to use a two-wire d.c. train bus, fed from an auxilliary generator and shared with other accessories. The heat should be applied to the car by using a resistance heating tape across the train bus.

Such a tape can be made up on the job by combining a double-faced pressure-sensitive mylar (3-M) tape about 1 inch wide with a band of aluminum foil (about 0.75″ wide and a commercially available thickness) and adhering the combination to the metal of the car. The length of tape needed is computed from Ohm's law and is applied to the car in any pattern desired, attempting to maintain spacings that will not often exceed about 6 inches. There is no presently available ready-made tape. There is no inherently superior pattern for the arrangement of the tape on the car body.

All the tape on a car can be a single electrical path, across the d.c. train bus, which can be of any voltage desired but it should not exceed 600 volts. The tape can be connected to the train bus by means of a simple nondetachable connector. There is no need to provide any heat modulation — it can use a simple on-off control sensitive to ambient temperature and if desired can be controlled for the entire train — individual car controls are not needed.

The alumium-mylar laminate, by itself, would present electrically live and hence dangerous parts but the entire car should be sprayed with urethane foam after the tape is applied. The foam serves as both thermal and electrical insulation.

This low-budget installation will require annual inspection and some patching. Urethane foam has the advantage of a closed-cell form, not needing any further weather protection. It can easily be patched with a portable spray-can repair kit. Annual inspection should include simple resistance measurements to verify the condition of the heating tape and to assist in either locating faults, if any, or identifying defects that require tape replacement.

The car need not and should not be painted before applying tape and foam. In modifying used cars, loose dirt and scale must be removed but the metal need not be bared.

## 2.3 Motive Power

For most near-future projects development costs will limit the choice to generally conventional diesel-electrics. For integral trains such power rarely is optimum. Some form of gas turbine is usually better but few individual projects can support the needed development. The appendix on next-generation equipment will treat gas turbine integral trains.

At contemporary cost relationships it will usually be advisable to overpower the train. This finding can be expected from economic studies in which time costs are properly assigned. Most prospective changes in power costs vis-à-vis other component costs will reinforce, not reverse, this relationship. The tradition of using minimum power (or less) is seldom economic. This is also true of conventional railroading but traditional costing obscures the fact.

### 2.3.1 Criteria

In general, it is most economic to select power on price per horsepower. Most very large diesel locomotives consist of two units on one frame and their higher price is "justified" by inapplicable economic computations. There is little competition in this field, hence little opportunity to shop for price, even on the basis of omission of the unneeded "extras."

Locomotives must be capable of sustained high speed and have high tractive effort capability. The need for good acceleration will limit usable horespower per axle; overselling of "high horsepower" should be avoided. It will seldom be found advisable, for example, to apply more than about 500 hp to one axle.

Until someone makes a suitable gas turbine unit available, there is no benefit in low-tare engines. This will come. But for the present, one must use diesel-electrics.

Locomotive selection criteria are:
Primary
  A — Reliability
  B — Cost per horsepower
Secondary
  C — Relative freedom from wheel slip
  D — Low maintenance requirements
  E — Fuel economy
  F — Longevity (high prospective salvage value)
Some comment on the significance of these criteria will help to understand the nature of the selection problem. It is probable that at any time some one locomotive from among those offered will be most suitable,

and a designer active in the field need only keep abreast of vendors' offerings. A new selection process for each project will seldom be needed, until it becomes feasible to select among types.

The reliability criterion refers to mission completion. Nearly any standard textbook on military hardware will elaborate this matter. Pragmatically, designers must review performance with particular attention to road failure experience — diesel-electrics are notorious for electrical system outages under adverse weather conditions, and reliability data, per se, are not available.

Cost per horsepower is simply total price divided by usable horsepower — most accessories are of little value except:

Dynamic brakes

Multiple-unit controls.

Manufacturers can gain advantage by eliminating such items as cabs, compressors (of half the units in an order), "B" unit conversion, etc., and reduce the price. As long as the sale of locomotives is organized as it is, manufacturers are unlikely to be willing to depart from established price relationships.

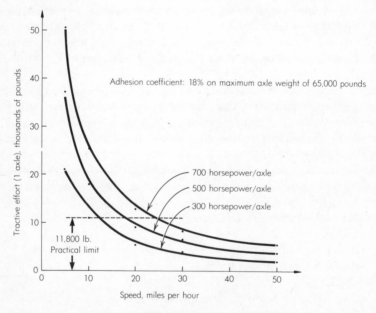

**2.3.1 — Speed/Tractive Effort Curves**

These curves display the relationship between force and speed when 1 horsepower is defined as 550 foot-pounds per second. One axle cannot be *relied* on for more than about 12,000 pounds tractive effort despite various test reports for ideal conditions. Effective use of all available power is important in starting and in recovering speed beyond limiting curves. Most integral train applications should use 300 to 500 horsepower per axle.

"Slip and slide" control is virtually standard but some models apply too much power to individual axles. Integral train service will often seek high acceleration in the interest of transit time, but axle loads seldom exceed 65,000 pounds and an adhesion factor higher than 18% is not reliable. A motored axle thus cannot reliably supply more than 11,800 pounds of tractive effort. One motored axle can effectively use 500 horsepower only at speeds of 16 mph and higher. Obviously high horsepower per axle will be of limited value.

Maintenance requirements can be estimated by review of manufacturers' claims and available experience data. However, evaluation should relate to reliability levels and other pertinent conditions of integral train service.

Fuel economy will not vary greatly among available units, and this criterion therefore is marginal until a choice of types is available.

The use of secondhand power must sometimes be considered. Such a choice is usually doubtful at best. Used power is often available at 30% to 40% of the price of new power but its maintenance cost will be high, its remaining service life will be short, and its reliability may be low. It may be seriously considered when utilizations are necessarily low or where road conditions force the use of light axle loads and contemporary units are difficult to apply.

### 2.3.2 Types and Accessories

**One basic motive power scheme uses locomotives, usually spaced out in the train, and the other uses powered cars. The powered-car types are usually capable of better economy but at present their adoption must await some single project that will support the needed development.**

A power block, so long as the choice is limited to diesels, will consist of two locomotives (usually six-axle types, 2,500 to 3,000 hp) and a tank car, for one full cycle or about 1 week, whichever is longer. Refined computations are unwarranted in sizing tanks. The following design procedure is adequate:

Determine the full-load fuel consumption of the units.

Determine the fuel consumption at several part-load levels —
e.g., idle, 25%, 50%, 75%.

Examine the profile and schedule of the route and estimate the number of hours in a cycle at each load level, with due allowance for delay times, empty train conditions, etc.

Multiply out the fuel requirements for each time segment;

Add about 10% to 15% for abnormal conditions;

Add fuel for supplying heat generators and other accessories.

This service can use low-pressure tanks on flatcars or skeleton cars —

they need not be pressure cars and need no heating coils or other usual tank car accessories. Car companies' efforts to sell "general purpose" tank cars should be resisted — this is the "sell-up." In general, tank cars will approach maximum allowable loads and tare reduction must be pursued.

Each power block will require the following accessories:

Repeater relays for train control signals — standard m.u. control will be used but the long cable will produce attenuation.

Fuel pumps and float switches to refill engine tanks from the tank car.

An engine-generator set to supply the train bus for heat and

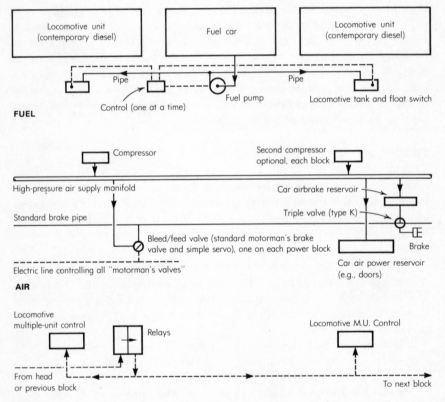

**FUEL**

**AIR**

**CONTROLS**

### 2.3.2 — Service Systems

This sketch shows, schematically, the arrangement of essential services for a power block composed of a fuel car and two locomotives. The fuel system is internal to the power block. The auxiliary electric heat and power line (not shown) is common to all — a train bus. The high air manifold is common to all and the airbrake piping is standard. The electrical controls come down the train to a repeater which passes the orders to the engines in the block and repeats them down-train to the next block.

other uses. The locomotive electrical system is not the best source; it produces full voltage only when additional load is least acceptable. At lower loads — and lower voltages — the heat will be inadequate because resistance heating output varies with the square of the voltage. Furthermore, controlling current reversals when not all engines operate at the same speed is not practical, and subdividing the train heat bus compromises reliability.

Electrically controlled brake pipe bleed valve.

Connections to feed a high-air train manifold.

The train will need:

An automatic system to sequence engines so that shutdown time will be divided among power blocks and so deplete the tank cars at about the same rate.

### 2.3.3 Sizing and Selection

**The number of motored axles is determined by ruling grades and/or desired accelerations, and total power is determined by speed. An in-train spare to protect the schedule is usually advantageous. It is not uncommon to compromise grade and speed requirements at ruling locations because economy usually rules out en route consist changes.**

Most integral train systems require 1.0 to 3.0 rated horsepower per total ton, with most of them using more than 1.5 and many of them more than 2.0. The design procedure is simple.

Determine the speed required on the longer grades. Allow additional equivalent grade for rolling resistance — usually about 0.3%. Convert to power thus:

$$\frac{2,000 \times p \times v \times 1.48}{550} = P = hp/ton$$

where p = grade (e.g., 2.5% = 0.025) plus rolling resistance
v = speed in miles per hour.

The net power available from one power block is estimated thus:

net power = $Pr \times E - (w \times P) = Pn$

where           Pr = rated power
E = efficiency from rating to rail
w = total weight of the power block
P = hp/ton above computed

Trailing load allowed per power block is:

$$\frac{Pn}{P} = Wt$$

where Pn = net power for the block
P = required power per ton
Wt = allowable trailing load per block

The power required on a short ruling grade must then be investigated if any such grades exist. It is inadvisable to plan on more than 11,800 pounds tractive effort per motored axle at 65,000 pounds gross. It is then necessary to determine whether the resulting speed on the ruling grade is acceptable.

When the number of *blocks* required ends in a fraction less than 0.5 (for two-engine power blocks), it will usually be adequate to round off to the next higher whole number of blocks. If it is more than 0.5, it is advisable to add one locomotive unit and a tank car past the next higher whole number of blocks.

### 2.4 Miscellaneous Transportation Plant Accessories

**It is usually economic to take the railroad as it is. There is seldom enough integral train potential traffic at one place to support major line improvement, but there will usually be a series of minor improvements that can produce justifying transit time savings. They will seldom be found through traditional channels.**

The subsection on marginal time capability improvements illustrates, again, the essential objectivity of economic computations and the importance of a system concept and economic orientation. Train time saved by, for example, applying an electric lock to eliminate a slow order is just as valuable as that gained by a costly grade reduction.

Fixed plant improvements made for an integral train system will also benefit other traffic. Hence perceptive railroads will want them on main lines, not on bypass lines. Designers must justify them on savings in integral train time, leaving benefits to other traffic as part of railroads' incentive — most railroad men are unaware of the value of time for conventional trains and any other course would be frustrating.

It is usually (not always) advisable to use new service and inspection facilities exclusively for an integral train. Designers will often be asked, *"Can* it be serviced at our existing shop?" The correct answer, "Yes," often leads to the assumption that the integral train must or should be so serviced. Mechanical men will seldom admit either to having unused capacity or the need to build what they will regard as a competing facility. Since most existing shops are less economical than a new facility, the "already overloaded" resistance is largely academic anyway. Expansion of an existing mechanical facility to serve an integral train is seldom economic.

### 2.4.1 Inspection and Service Facilities

**Service facilities dispense fuel and supplies, perform preventive maintenance, and provide a home for spare parts. They are best located**

at one terminal or common point per system, separate from general-purpose railroad facilities. Inspection elsewhere usually is a nonfunctional formality — e.g., the ICC's 500-mile "inspection."

To pursue this example, the "500-mile" inspection "facility" consists of a trackside jeep road one train length long, located where the train can stop without unacceptably blocking a crossing. It will use one inspector and auto for 1 day, which can include travel.

A service facility is another matter. It may or may not be located adjacent to a terminal. It should be located where the train(s) will pass it on empty segments, preferably.

The principal components of a service facility are:

Fueling station
Inspection bay
Car body shop
Wheel shop
Engine shop
Electronic and control shop
Cripple and ready tracks.

The fueling station will need tankage for bunkering one or more trains — usually part of the price of the fuel. It should be equipped for fast loading of tank cars — a dispensing device something like the waterspout once used for locomotives is suitable. The tank cars will have large manholes in them and the filling spout should load a 100-ton tank car while the adjacent parts of the train are being routinely inspected — generally a few minutes. Station design includes determination of the number of train elements to be in the working area at one time.

The inspection bay will contain a through track on which part of the train can stand for inspection of controls, engines, wheels, etc. In severe climates it will need enclosure; it will require shelter anywhere. The scheme calls for the train to be advanced until a power block is in fueling position. Then the power block and associated cars are inspected before the train is moved up again, handling the train in a series of cycles. Switching is done during moves.

The facility needs shop space apart from the path of trains moving through the station. Here engines, wheels, car bodies and controls can be repaired, and cars rotated to shop status can be placed for scheduled or unscheduled repair work.

The facility needs tracks on which

available or "ready" power blocks can be placed for switching into the train,

available or "ready" car blocks can be placed for switching into the train,

car and power blocks can be switched out for later shop spotting,

rail-delivered supplies can be received.
Track through the inspection/service bay arranged to handle
the train intact is also needed.

At low utilizations, one use of unsold time is to service the train at an existing facility. Such an arrangement is usually associated with low volumes, modified secondhand equipment, and low-pressure schedules.

There will rarely, if ever, be need for helper engines or similar services; hence no need for facilities to service them.

The integral train will not use yards, existing enginehouses, etc. When this matter arises, the designer can assume that communications have failed and he is misunderstood.

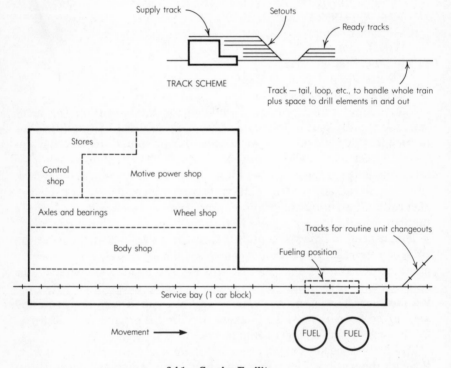

2.4.1 — Service Facility

In use, the train is passed intermittently through such a facility, stopping with a section or block in the service bay while it is inspected and fueled, supplies are put aboard, subsystems are tested, etc. Then the train moves under its own power to bring the next section into the bay, meanwhile switching out any elements that are due or are found by inspection to require important repairs. The "back shop" should include facilities for wheel, body, power, control, and other work. Track layout must provide separate tracks for ready power and trailer blocks to be conveniently switched in, and a place to put elements switched out — they can move into the shop when the train is gone. Work stations should be planned for economy of train time, since train time cost usually dominates. For example, the fueling station should use large, manhole-size openings in the tank and should load like engines once loaded water. Such a facility will count time in minutes, not hours.

## 2.4.2 Upgrading

Line improvement justification depends almost entirely on transit time. Major structural improvements can seldom be justified, nor can such costly work as new rail, CTC, grade reduction and major bridge strengthening, because lower cost alternates are usually available. A weak bridge can be avoided — use a competing line — a steep hill can be negotiated by using enough power, by climbing it lightly loaded, by using another line, or by giving up time. Integral trains use so little track maintenance that line improvements directed to maintenance savings will seldom survive analysis for inclusion in integral train budgets.

Line improvements with noneconomic justification are generally limited to passing sidings — and then only on single track where integral trains themselves will meet. No matter how long an integral train may be, it can pass any train at any siding so long as one of them is shorter than the siding.

Frequently used passing sidings should be about 1.5 (shorter) train lengths long and occasionally used sidings need be only 1.0 train length long. It will usually be more economical to lengthen existing sidings than to build new.

Improvements made for transit time saving are evaluated like any other investment. The formula is:

$$V = \frac{2 \times n \times Vt \times t}{R}$$

where n = number of round trips per year

Vt = value of the train's time in dollars per minute

t = number of minutes to be saved per passage

R = rate of "return" required, generally 12% to 15% for improvements of this kind

V = capital value justified

Any improvements whose value exceeds their estimated cost should be made — and paid for out of integral train system capital.

Projects that do not satisfy this criterion should be referred to the railroad. It can evelute them for its own implementation, justifying some of them by using the time-bonus that the integral train system will offer *plus* their value to other traffic.

Projects for this purpose are discovered by examining the situation directly, usually in the field. Division superintendents and other railway forces can offer only limited direct help — few of them have been expected to think in minutes, and the opportunities are found in terms of minutes. "Big deals" are rare. Some possibilities to review — and to suggest others — are:

Surfacing to improve a speed limit

Applying electric locks to improve a speed limit in a yard

Applying crossing warnings to improve a speed limit

Repairing special work to improve a speed limit

Providing better personal access to speed up a crew change

Applying rail anchors to permit more vigorous braking at a critical location

Replacing a turnout with a longer one — the long train can profit considerably by the improved speed limit

Adding repeater signals at critical locations

Repairing joints

### 2.4.3 Shared and New Track Rationale

**Track installed or retained for an integral train must be budgeted as an integral train cost (capital and maintenance) despite the fact that it may be used by other traffic. The capital cost of existing track kept in service when it would have been abandoned is equal to net salvage. When an integral train shares track also needed for other traffic, any improvements made for the integral train must be budgeted to it. Incremental maintenance of shared track must be budgeted to the integral train in incremental cost budgets.**

A rigorous treatment of this matter is usually important beyond its relative size. Departures from this rationale must be individually supported lest problems in negotiating charges or making economic choices become uncontrollable.

New track will be of a quality that the integral train requires — more or less than on other parts of the railroad. It will incur "initial maintenance" as well as incremental maintenance but must not be assigned any allocated cost — e.g., station painting.

When a track would have been abandoned except for the integral train, it must be treated as if it were bought from the railroad at net salvage and treated like any other investment. Controversy over whether a line would or would not be kept in service must be resolved realistically. An integral train plan must not be treated as a rare opportunity to be "bailed out" of unprofitable investments. In a system where several patrons are served, the costs — particularly those associated with branches — should be figured in detail and budgeted to the traffic that uses them.

Track that would be kept in service anyway — "shared" track — is budgeted with incremental costs separated from contributions to fixed costs.

It will seldom be advisable to upgrade significantly any main or secondary track for an integral train. Enough physical improvement to produce significant transit time saving will usually be a major operation difficult to justify.

It is sometimes necessary or economically advisable to upgrade minor routes needed for integral train service as part of long hauls. The cost of such improvements is treated like any upgrading. For example, a 10-mile "bridge" that would force a 1,000-mile system to use inferior equipment justifies serious attention.

Sometimes it will be found advisable to improve maintenance standards in the interest of transit time improvement. In such cases the maintenance budgeted to the integral train will consist of two parts. One is the incremental maintenance traceable to the passage of traffic over the line. The other is the maintenance that would not be done except to hold a higher standard of track condition.

In cases where such maintenance improvement cannot be fully justified by integral train savings the matter should be referred to the railroad. It can consider potential income from integral train time-bonuses plus the value of the improvements for its other traffic.

## 2.5 Scheduling

**The dominance of time costs emphasizes the importance of scheduling. As usual in engineering, anyone can produce a "conservative" design. The engineer's real tasks are to estimate time actually needed and to devise means of minimizing the time consumed.**

Attainable schedules must be estimated separately for each line and service. There are various ways to make schedules, but experience is important — there is no reliable mechanistic system. Among other reasons, an inexperienced estimator can seldom make the railroad men, on whom he must depend for locally unique input data, adequately aware of either:

A — The concept of attainable as distinguished from past performance.

B — The idea that better equipment can produce better performance — and sometimes even that there *can be* better equipment.

Designers are cautioned against indiscriminate use of external data, such as machine runs or simulations. Excessively "conservative" data can enable operating men to be essentially indifferent to time or can inadequately exploit the capabilities of superior equipment.

## 2.5.1 Existing Schedules

**An integral train can usually improve on existing performance. One scheme is to use historic passenger schedules as first approximation — a designer will find use of a copy of the "Official Guide" for about 1950. At that time most routes still had passenger trains whose performance**

suggests physical limits of each route. An integral train can usually improve on those times, often considerably.

When examining passenger schedules for clues to attainable time, designers are cautioned to evaluate time lost in the many station stops that characterize most passenger train schedules.

Existing freight performances are limited by the unreliability and capabilities of random cars. Designers are also cautioned in the matter of freight train terminal (and intermediate yard time) allowances. These allowances are not always *stated* in the schedules but they are in overall timetables. The integral train will be "relayed" at terminals and will also usually improve on running time.

### 2.5.2  Data Collection

Gathering scheduling data is an art, not a science. Present and past performance data, block records and train sheets, published timetables and on-time records will be useful but must not be assigned applicability they do not have. Integral trains, for example, do little or no intermediate work, experience no yard delays, and are not held for connections. An important resource is a library of timetables. Designers will benefit from informed and informal discussions with *local* operating men on the theme of what *could* be done — with some intellectual rapport. Without such rapport that source of data is unreliable.

Personal observation of train movements in the affected area — by a knowledgeable man, preferably unescorted — will suggest sources of delay and opportunities to improve on what local supervision will sometimes consider optimum.

A designer usually should personally visit the route — he will soon learn to recognize some conditions.

> *For example:* Weed-grown gravel ballast characterizes a line where good time cannot be had cheaply. A neat shoulder line and rock ballast characterizes well-maintained track where good speed can be had, even on light track.

Designers should confer with terminal supervision and consult available operating records, time slips, etc.

> *For example:* A record of trains held out at major yards will suggest a frequently blocked main track and consequent unreliable schedules.

As noted, there is no way but to research the matter by interview; by visit, sometimes riding over the line; and by the use of some judgment, which will improve with experience. There is a system that fits well into most situations. The normal procedure is:

> Start with sales or traffic vice-presidents. They should be reassured in person and in writing that neither costs nor rates

will be discussed with anyone but them. The integral train researcher is completely uninterested in what it does cost or what it has cost to carry traffic. Sometimes a "potential new traffic" condition will elicit the needed cooperation.

He should be asked to introduce the researcher to the operating vice-president. He, too, should be assured that there is no intention to ask the railroad what it costs to run a train — the railroad does not know anyway. The interest is in capabilities. He should be reassured that one of the purposes of the work is to make sure that recommendations will not include any that could not be carried out at the operating level. Of all the objectives of an integral train investigation this is the one that will most interest operating executives.

The operating vice-president should be asked to refer the researcher to men on the next level — regional or district operating men who, in turn, will refer the researcher to division superintendents and sometimes to trainmasters and others.

Every operating official involved should be interviewed at needed length. Time should be allowed to make sure that each man visited thoroughly understands just what is contemplated in his territory — not just to gather the needed information. The actuality will nearly always be less formidable than the unknown.

The researcher must obtain his information in this way. But he must also leave behind him a group of operating officials who will be his enthusiastic supporters. An integral train system, if properly planned, will be attractive to operating men, and their support in the "idea-peddling" stages will be needed.

Operating men will be asked for timetables, maps, profiles and track charts for study. The profiles and track charts will first be examined rather superficially to find ruling grades and obtain a generalized idea of the line — curvature, rise and fall, sustained grades, etc. Governing physical conditions are not always the same for integral trains as for other traffic — e.g., ruling grades shorter than the train do not "govern." Operating men will be encouraged to discuss what they could do with a generously powered train of good cars (in terms of transit time); they will be encouraged to talk informally until the researcher learns about anomalies.

*For example:* One investigation encountered surprising resistance on a single division. It developed that this superintendent was repairing cars on the main track — his supervision was so poor that switching the cars into the yard was unreliable. He did not want any more mainline traffic that might force him to make changes — after years of sloppy operation, any improvement risked labor trouble.

Records showing number of delays traceable to slides, delayed connections, bridge openings, passenger movements, and the like, should be sought. An interest in records will rapidly moderate some of the more extreme "impression" testimony about how hard it is to run any trains at all.

### 2.5.3 Machine Runs and Similar Material

Many railroads have used their computers to simulate train performances. The variables are line conditions, power-weight ratios, car factors, and train size. Such runs usually show a theoretical time — integral trains can sometimes improve on them and sometimes they cannot.

Some programmers are conservative to a degree justified by conventional conditions but not by integral train conditions. This writer has found such data useful, but an experienced estimator, using "seat of the pants" judgment, can reach findings very close to the theoretical findings. When using such material designers should confer with the electronic data processing men. Quite often unsuspected communications problems exist and the machine-produced data is not what executives think it is.

### 2.5.4 Allowances

Schedule projections must allow for the unforeseen — undue precision is an exercise in futility. Any projected schedule must be increased by a delay allowance. Integral train speed limits can exceed established freight train limits — one design task is to design a train that *can* get over the road faster. Delay allowances — matters of judgment — in general will be in the 5% to 20% range — usually less than 10%. Resisters — some lacking understanding and some seeking an undemanding schedule — will cite many dire combinations of circumstances to support the premise that there should be *no* schedule.

Delay allowances should be specific. It may be convenient to lump them together in budgets, but they should be quite specific in concept.

Allowances that will be suggested include:

For crew calling — reject because the crew should be on hand when the train arrives.

For en route fuel and mechanical servicing — reject; the train should be serviced at its own facility.

To clear some allegedly congested time or place — reject, but assign a realistic transit time — and reject proposals to dawdle en route to arrive at a preferred time.

For mechanical breakdown — assign realistically low in view

of the relatively high-quality equipment and maintenance to
be used.

For adapting to fixed schedules of other trains — allow, but
insist that the allowance be based on the printed timetable.

*For example:* A superintendent insisted on clearing the
times of trains on his card — but the timecard showed conflicts.
He then said that the trains never moved on schedule but required all the 24 hours daily because they could appear at random times. The argument did not last long.

Unassigned delay allowances will usually be needed but must be
assigned to each division or district in the scheduling process. A railroad should be encouraged to eliminate them by using a time bonus.
That rate is the "cost of time" for trains whose space-available time is
sold to interruptible or "dump rate" patrons. When the system cannot
use such time, the base rate should leave room for incentive anyway —
few, including railroad, managements will function at their best with no
incentive.

### 2.6 Train Design

**Train design comprises selection, sizing, component arrangement, and
choice of control systems. There is obviously no standard design nor is
there any useful reply to such questions as "How long is an integral
train?" or "Is it a 100-ton car?"**

Train design starts with sizing — it should usually be as large as can
be kept busy. Use the best attainable schedule and train size is annual
traffic divided by attainable number of cycles. Since schedule depends
on train design, a series of converging approximations is usually necessary. When the size so determined is under 10,000 tons net it is usually
advisable to study alternatives — e.g., slower times (reduction in motive
power), idle time, or sharing with other users. The typical case for
single-purpose use cannot be considered probably secure until train size
exceeds 30,000 tons.

Terminal conditions will sometimes introduce discontinuities in cost-
size curves. Reversal of the cost-size curve will seldom be reached.

Power should usually be dispersed in the train — at minimum one
power block at each end. Maximum power block size will seldom exceed 5,000 hp — fixed by the capacity of a tank car to carry fuel for a
service cycle or avoidance of concentrations of tractive effort. Unless
power is dispersed under the payload, concentrations should not exceed
12 motored axles in a block. Fuel cars should not be motorized.

Control system simplicity is an objective in itself. For example, when
all driven axles can be uniformly loaded, there need be no individual
motor control. Engine controls should be fail-safe, closed-circuit types

using cable and repeaters. Radio and draft-sensitive systems are seriously inferior, especially in large trains. Unit cycling to deplete fuel tanks uniformly is usually needed.

### 2.6.1 Train Size

**As noted above, optimum train size is usually the largest that can be kept busy — in one trade or several. Such elements as siding length, drawbar pull, or other traditional limits on train size are largely irrelevant. Conventional air brake limitations do not govern when a dual line and/or dispersed, controllable power is used whereby the train pipe can be charged or reduced from several locations. Most practical operating men prefer a few very large to many medium-size trains. Terminals seldom govern train size, since economy usually demands facility or operating adaptations — provided a system concept awareness prevents division of responsibility.**

A previous section reviewed the mechanics of selecting train size — it will sometimes lead to very large sizes, especially when a diversity of uses is available. Past design work has developed cases in which the optimum train size is in the range of 50,000 to 80,000 payload tons. Terminal conditions become increasingly limiting for very large trains. Eight to 10 miles long is probably the limit for some time to come, though there is theoretically no limit.

When new equipment is used the integral train system can avoid most of the traditional limiting factors, of which drawbar capacity and system reliability have been the most inhibiting. Planners should resist proposals to limit train size to fit existing sidings, and to carry this point must also insist on captive, even if not new, equipment, in the interest of reliability. Most existing lines have sidings so short that such a limitation would be grotesquely small — this is not a matter of making a *small* concession to existing conditions and prejudices. Once it is understood that existing siding length must be exceeded, knowledgeable operating men will favor longer and fewer trains, especially in high-density territory. The operative consideration here will be train reliability. A conventional train is so unreliable that any prudent operating man *must* have a place to put it.

The idea is prevalent that size economy is mainly crew cost. Crew cost does decline with increasing size, but this is not the only nor sometimes even the principal source of economy — as some reflection will show. Other elements are efficiency in use of power, minimizing traffic delays, and reducing terminal operating cost.

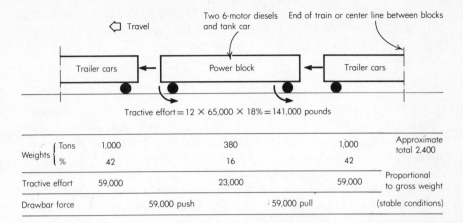

Tractive effort = 12 × 65,000 × 18% = 141,000 pounds

| Weights { | Tons | 1,000 | 380 | 1,000 | Approximate total 2,400 |
|---|---|---|---|---|---|
| | % | 42 | 16 | 42 | |
| Tractive effort | | 59,000 | 23,000 | 59,000 | Proportional to gross weight |
| Drawbar force | | 59,000 push | 59,000 pull | | (stable conditions) |

### 2.6.2 — Tractive Effort Distribution

A power block using 12 motored axles on two diesel-electric units will normally transmit only 59,000 pounds to the draft gear at each end. When the power is under the payload the force at the ends of the power block can be even lower. This condition permits cars to be designed for low buffing forces to reduce tare, cost, and risk of damage.

### 2.6.2  Power Arangement

Power block size limitation controls structural demands to permit lower cost and lower-tare cars. It also permits slack control — by setting controls to keep the train either stretched out or closed up — and it also limits the amount of slack between control points. Combined with heavy power ratios, power dispersal permits approaching a tight-lock train in which adequate power substitutes for the essentially fragile, marginal design of conventional freight trains.

Power blocks should be spaced as nearly uniformly in the train as possible. This policy, combined with a limitation on power block size, will control draft concentrations. For example, if power blocks are limited to 12 motored axles, the tractive effort of one power block will be limited to:

$$12 \times 65,000 \times 18\% = 141,000 \text{ pounds}$$

Typically, a power block will be buried in the middle of a group of cars and its tractive effort will be applied ahead and behind it. Furthermore, some of its tractive effort will be used to move the power block itself. At common power ratios and weight relationships one power block carrying 5,000 hp will be used for 2,000 to 2,500 tons and the power block itself will weigh 380 tons or so.

Therefore about 80% of the tractive effort will be divided between the two end drawbars, or only about 60,000 pounds each. It is sometimes desirable to use a half-block, if practical, at each end of the train, to limit tractive effort concentration when conventional engines are used

and an end control cab would be awkward to provide on a car.
Fuel cars can use six-wheel trucks, but for most designs more or less common four-axle tank cars will be adequate.

### 2.6.3 Controls

The engineman's control panel can and should look quite conventional. No special training or skill can be assumed. All such — to him exotic — elements as power cycling, partial shutdowns (as in gas turbine trains) and remote braking must be automatic. Small diesel train control will be entirely conventional except for the repeater relays made necessary by the long m.u. wires. More sophisticated trains will use sequence control, power-level controls, brake monitoring and such — all automatic.

The train needs a control cab at each end. It may be the cab that comes with a locomotive or it may be provided for the purpose. The advantage of a separate cab, built into a payload car, is that it permits placing the power back in the train where its tractive effort is used on both sides and where it does not encounter slippery rail. Such a cab can be fitted with standard control gear. Engine inaccessibility is not material.

The control cab will need the following, besides the usual gear:

Gauge for the high-air manifold

Train-phone (preferably wired)

Direction control handle to make one end of the train or the other operative at a time

Door lockout control (for manual and automatic-door bulk trains).

Elements not visible to the engineman will include:

Sequence control for sophisticated trains to shut down some of the engines (for gas turbines) or assign loads at part-load conditions (for diesel systems)

Air compressor sequencing control — not all compressors on the train will be needed to maintain air in the tanks and high-air manifold most of the time

Electrical controls on the brake handle for remote control of corresponding valves down the train, in each power block.

The electric brake control system will consist, usually, of a simple bleed/feed valve on the train pipe at each power block, electrically controlled to allow the entire brake pipe to be emptied at once. The next level of sophistication uses a servo to cause a standard motorman's valve at each power block to follow the one at the front cab. It is not advisable to subdivide the train pipe.

The high-air system uses an unsubdivided manifold extending the length of the train and connecting to all the air compressors which automatically maintain its pressure. The manifold will serve as a source of air to keep all air tanks filled, controlled by an automatic valve on each tank. It is also a source of air for pneumatic doors where they are used.

Engine control will use standard m.u. controls. A relay assembly on each power block will receive the signals at attenuated voltage (because of the long cable) and pass them on down-train and to the engines on the block. A control cable and standard connector will be located on each end of each block (and hence on each end of the train) so the integral train or any block can be coupled *ahead* of any standard m.u.-equipped engine and function normally, should such handling be necessary.

All cables and brake and control lines will comprise fail-safe systems. The standard train pipe is, itself, such a system. The high-air manifold will be equipped with pressure-flow gauges so that if it is broken a supervisory circuit will open and the train will stop. Electrical and heating cables will carry supervisory circuits so that if a cable is parted or a connector is opened the train will stop. Angle valves will be provided for air lines. Receptacles on the cars for cable ends will be wired to serve the same purpose for the wire lines — a loose cable end must be plugged in to close a supervisory circuit before the train will move.

### 2.6.4 Miscellaneous

**The integral train must perform as a unit, and will have various accessories intended to make it so perform as well as to enhance its efficiency and safety beyond previous levels. It will, for example, usually use such items as wired train phones (no "dead spots"). New or extensively modified cars will be equipped with riding platforms, ground-access hand brakes (car-dropping will be prohibited — and prevented), spare parts, and other specialties.**

Designers should provide for telephone jacks at frequent intervals along the train, preferably accessible from riding platforms (or brake steps if used). Brakemen can thus talk to the engineman and conductor readily and reliably. Reliance on radio is inadvisable in the integral train system where the fixed consist permits the use of a more sophisticated system. Radios are exposed to interference, "dead spots" and other annoying problems best avoided when opportunity is offered.

Hand brakes, if used at all, should be accessible only from the ground. This provision, together with the use of sizable car blocks, will prevent the dangerous practices of "flying in" and car-dropping — which should never be needed anyway.

A preferred alternate to hand brakes is the use of skates to set off cripples — which will be about the only use for hand brakes. The high air line will permit parking on air, and cars, except cripples and shop cars, will seldom be handled individually.

The train, especially if it is of new-design components, should carry spare parts for critical and unusual elements. Equipment should be locked to minimize unauthorized "repair" work, but work will be necessary occasionally and the required tools should be on the train. Relays, truck parts when specialized, fittings for the high air line, electric valves and the like should be carried. They should be used by repairmen along the way only after receiving telephoned instructions from the train's management.

## 2.7 Operations

Integral train operation need not be vastly different from conventional train operation — just closer to an operating man's fondest dream. The integral train will be operated the way most operating men wish they could operate all trains. It will differ, though, from what conventional operation actually is. To avoid overstating costs, designers must take care to assure that railway officials involved understand just what — and how little — is expected and what the designer intends. It is often assumed that the integral train is a "rate gimmick" and that operations changes will not actually be involved. The traffic is *not* to be forced into traditional patterns.

A central tenet of railroading has long been that cars are normally standing and their movement from one parking lot to another is quite a

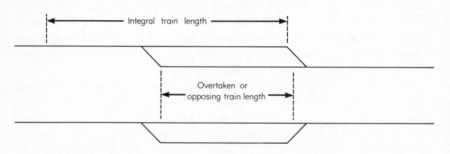

2.7 — Sidings

The first arrival at a siding must wait if the block ahead is occupied by an opposing train. If one train is longer than the siding, the other must be shorter. Economy demands that the longer train use the route with the higher speed limit, though it is sometimes difficult to distinguish between "main" and "siding." Many generalities will be offered as "horrible examples" about how "everything" must go into a siding for the integral train. The same rules apply even to a light engine, though. Meeting points are still subject to the usual laws of physics and meets are still *one at a time*. But an integral train will force some serious thought about the value of train time. The time-bonus payment will even lead to sidetracking slow — e.g., local passenger — trains to let the integral train overtake and pass.

project. The first operating man's question in a planning conference typically is "Where do I park it?" (Answer: "You don't.") A central tenet of integral train philosophy is that a train is a unit( like an ocean vessel) whose normal state is in motion, even loading and unloading. When it stops its managers should be concerned. The difference is large. Especially when an operating man thinks an hour or two a day is "constant use."

An operating man — e.g., division superintendent — can be told:
"All you want to see is the rear end going down the next division. You don't supply the fuel nor the power. You just supply the driver, and you go to the junction after the train with a taxicab, not a locomotive. It is not 'hook and haul'; it is 'get on and drive.' You will be paid for speed. And it is purposely too big to lose or fit your yard, and your brakemen can't take it apart — just get rid of it."

### 2.7.1 Crews and Crew Changes

No improvement in existing labor agreements is assumed. The same crews will run integral trains as run other trains — sometimes "next out" and sometimes assigned crews. At crew-changes, outbound crewmen will be delivered, in advance, to the two ends of the train, by taxicab, to be there *before the train stops*. The same taxis will take the arriving crewmen to their time clocks. It will seldom be profitable to call a crew after the train has arrived or otherwise make the train wait for men.

Budgets should use existing labor agreements despite high labor cost and low productivity of labor. Productivity, traditionally figured, will be high, but it is equipment productivity, not labor productivity. The conductor has little to do and the fireman even less. Still, all planning should assume no changes in this respect. The train can use two men effectively but five should be budgeted.

Each division must supply an estimated time of arrival to the next, so that crews can be called. In figuring time penalty and bonus, proper forecast arrival times must be considered, lest the time saved be unusable or ITD be incurred.

The compelling reason it is seldom economic to use a crew already on duty (e.g., a yard crew for a transfer) is the delay to the integral train. A more visible, and to some people more believable, reason is the fact that most railroads pay an arbitrary fraction of a day for an engineman getting off one engine and getting on another. And the integral train will always use its own power.

The train telephone will assist in the departure brake test and in assuring that all crewmembers are aboard. Nonstop changes are possible and, in some cases, advisable.

## 2.7.2  Maintenance

Programmed maintenance will require each element — power block, car block or control car — to be rotated out on schedule. Cyclic in-train inspection will normally find other elements that need attention out of schedule. All but the most elementary work will be done out of the train. All but emergency work will be done at a specialized facility provided for the integral train in nearly all cases.

The integral train service facility will see each train on a schedule, for routine "trip" inspection. Additionally every power and car block will be rotated out of service on a schedule. At that time wheels, engines and controls — all parts of the equipment — will be subjected to a prescribed service routine. Wheels will be dropped out and changed on schedule. Overhauls, monthly inspections, lubricant changes, body paint, door maintenance — all items will be serviced out of the train on a rigid schedule. The controlled service makes it possible to relate these cycles to time, mileage and load cycles. It is not necessary to resort to breakdown maintenance nor to limit maintenance to inspectors' rejects. The use of large and hence few blocks of cars and fixed-consist power blocks reduces the amount of record-keeping to a minimum.

Using a computer to direct routine maintenance is an affectation even in conventional railroading. For an integral train system of even considerable complexity, maintenance control is simply another minor clerical task for a maintenance shop office.

Trip-service accorded each train every trip has two functions. Its primary function is to replenish supplies of fuel, sand and water and incidentally to check and service such things as batteries and lubricants. Its secondary function is to check out and make minor repairs on control circuits, wheels, doors and other mechanical elements. Any repairs that would delay the train will cause the unit to be rotated for out-of-train repair. When planning systems, an equipment inventory allowance must be made for off-schedule maintenance requirements.

### 2.7.3  Wrecks and Mishaps

The integral train is not immune — it can be hit by a truck at a crossing or run into a rock just like any other train. But when such an event does occur it has a few advantages which make it easier to cope with the problem.

Wrecks and mishaps include both accidents and road failures. No system is immune, but the function of the cyclic maintenance is to minimize road failures.

When the integral train is damaged in a collision, there is nothing for it but to clear the track and proceed. The integral train, though, has one small element in its favor: its rear end can be driven out under its own power.

When an equipment failure occurs, the matter of liability must be established just as it would be for any accident for which the responsibility is in dispute.

It should be noted that when a crossing accident impends, the integral train, with its simultaneous braking, can apply its brakes sooner and so avoid some accidents and minimize some that could not be avoided in any case. It is not practical to assign a money value to this improvement but it is real nonetheless.

Better maintenance and controlled service conditions, together with such details as unit brakes (no dragging brake rigging), sealed bearings and the like, will reduce the exposure to road failures that may cause wrecks. Similarly the dispersed power can reduce the amount of slack available for run-in — minimizing another source of accident.

### 2.7.4 Supervision and Coordination

In crowded or complex areas supervision may be used to monitor an integral train's movements and initiate needed instructions. In general, procedures and routes should be chosen to minimize such needs. The often-heard suggestions that a traveling supervisor accompany the train at all times is rarely, if ever, appropriate. It will not need supplementary power and its equipment cannot be "borrowed," to further insulate it from the usual crisis-to-crisis operation. When a supervisor is needed for a specific condition he is budgeted at 1 day and expenses for each such occasion.

Someone — normally shipper or owner — must assign a liaison man, at least part-time. He must be cognizant of the train's hour-to-hour movements. As the industry grows more accustomed to integral trains, it is reasonable to expect this need to increase — as long as an integral train is novel and "special" it wil get some attention automatically. And its time value justifies close attention, even after it is no longer noval.

Real concern with utilization and its corollaries should pervade the industry even now, but it is neglected in conventional railroading where the effects of neglect can be effectively concealed. For proper use of an integral train system there is no choice but to "keep on top of it."

### 2.7.5 Atypical Operations

A "typical" integral train system will use one train, each trip carrying one commodity from one origin to one destination (though the next trip may involve a different commodity, source and destination). This section can review only a few of many variations — to stimulate imaginative designers to devise programs for their own unique needs.

A few examples, each briefly outlined, are:

A train can be made up of car blocks, each the size of the trestle at its owner's blast furnace plant. The cars can be filled at an off-site raw material station so that they are in the correct order without switching. Each setting can then be used as received without in-plant switching.

Wheat can be loaded at country elevators into selected cars at each, not necessarily consecutively, to produce the desired blend when the cars are discharged in train order.

Continuing the wheat example, a delivery station can be equipped with two hoppers — one for "normal" wheat and one for rejected cars as determined by analysis of samples while the train is en route. The doors on "reject" cars can be set to open at the second hopper.

Deliveries to various users can be handled in the reverse of the grain loading operation. Obviously a diversified operation can be developed in which various commodities are loaded at various points and delivered to various points, the principal requirement being that the whole constitute a continuous route.

# 3. MONEY

There is no "true" cost. Most cost calculations seek to estimate the cost effect of alternatives or to supply "ammunition" for negotiations. Cost calculations are used at all stages, and seldom are ends in themselves. The techniques most often found useful are derived from construction cost estimating, not from transportation, economic or industrial procedures. Budget sections of reports must be presented in considerable detail to show that all needs have been budgeted, to assist in dividing the task commercially and to protect the proposals from attacks based on differences of opinion in trivial matters. It is, furthermore, seldom necessary to estimate consequential delays because it is usually quite clearly cheaper to avoid them. Fortunately, single-purpose, readily budgeted facilities are usually most economic.

Most economists, when they concern themselves with costs at all, use factors representing past experience — usually averages at that. This practice denies the potential for improvement. It should be axiomatic that the way any job is done and the tools used determine what it will cost. In transportation few men now living have seen substantive technological change, and "costs" are widely but incorrectly thought to be immutable — the "mature science" notion. Imputing "experience" costs to new methods will always find that the proposed innovation is not economic — it assumes so to start.

Most railroad cost men estimate in terms of train-miles, gross ton-miles, average man-hours, or other factors that have been standardized for their own lines. Consultants who derive transportation expertise from traditional sources use similar devices — sometimes adding experience elsewhere in circumstances that may not be applicable. "Costs" so derived inherently resemble the costs of what went before — the "constants" were selected on the assumption of "no change" — even though the premise is not articulated.

An integral train budget must be compiled much like a building contractor estimates a bid. The process is different from usual railroad costing and it is difficult to overstate the importance of understanding it. This system is used for the same reason the contractor uses it — it reflects and hence permits exploiting the economic benefits of technological improvement.

*For example:* An economist projects the cost of apartments at some price per cubic foot. A contractor bidding a job adds up details. He knows, for instance, that reducing ceiling height 10% does not reduce costs 10% as the economist's formula indicates. The economist's formula postulates that no such change will be made, hence is not suited to evaluating the change.

An integral train cost estimator must add up details. If he plans to use "standard factors" he might as well not make any substantive improvements — he can "prove" that none *can* be made that will affect costs.

*For example:* Larger wheels can reduce track maintenance costs. A railroad staff engineer demanded that the big cars have big wheels to reduce track maintenance but insisted on charging the project for track maintenance at "standard" rates. He could not comprehend the concept of quantifying differences.

The largest component of integral train costs will be time costs. This is, to some extent, true of all railroading, but most railroad costing conceals the fact. Correct computation of these costs and a series of cost-oriented design decisions will force great stress on utilization, at an operative, specific (not diffuse nor generalized) level. The only other individually important costs are fuel and crews — the latter being virtually proportional to mileage, plus arbitraries.

Though remaining elements are individually small, overall figures or blanket allowances are seldom satisfactory. The budget must not only be correct, it must also be convincing. Seeming to omit even a trivial item or to "bury" it by combining it with other small items helps a self-interested or defensive critic to discredit the entire program without real basis.

*For example:* Very little is known about wheel life in conventional service. This writer has heard reputable railroad men assert, with great conviction, wheel costs that vary by a factor of more than 100.

*For example:* A plausible-sounding report by a respected organization assigned an incredible sum to track maintenance. On questioning, the project engineer admitted that since he knew no way to estimate this cost he had used a number large enough to produce the desired finding — he was "conservatively high." His objective was to support a profit claim — a valid objective, but detectable intellectual dishonesty lost him his case.

There is no substitute for diligent, resourceful, competent estimators because there is no mechanistic system presently known that can assure having all the items, much less having them correctly. The estimate is no more reliable than the man who makes it. It is not a task for a committee, a bookkeeper or a "research team." It is an art, at least in part, and individually practiced.

Fortunately, most of the elements are individually small and can be estimated reasonably closely by a knowledgeable and perceptive person even — or especially — without detailed, specialized, railroad experience. A traditional "engineer type" with no judgment or confidence in his judgment cannot cope with the problem — nor can a committee.

## 3.1 Ownership Costs

**Ownership costs run with time — all the time. There is no such thing as free time. They can be treated as imputed rent, at some number of dollars per hour or minute. Ownership cost for any operation is the product of the time cost times the total number of hours or minutes used, including unproductive time required. Thus the time assigned to a function must include its delay allowance, along with other time used by *or for* the function. It is advisable to state delay allowances for each function separately and avoid overall ratios.**

*For example:* If local labor agreements require a crosstown "yard" crew, the choices are to call a crew or to use a crew already on duty. The latter usually involves lower labor cost but delays the train. "Transit time" in such a case must show the delay allowance used and its cost, plus the labor cost with which it is associated. Then a special crew will usually be called — it usually costs less.

Even a basement machine shop charges time in terms of *sold hours*. All of an integral train's time is available for sale and hence "sold hours" must total

$$24 \times 365 = 8,760 \text{ hours per year}$$

Shop time is sold, too — to the repair function, and that service in turn is sold to each mission. Here is one of the places where the existing facility will become noncompetitive — few are organized around the premise that time costs money.

A decision to hold a train somewhere is supposed to be an economic decision. Such proposals will abound. This is just one more situation in which an integral train planner must insist on an economically logical analysis.

*For example:* Someone usually wants the train passed through an area he considers unique at a specific time of day. He will usually understand that if the train waits nearby — where he can see it — it uses time and hence money. He must be shown that if it dawdles en route it is still using time and hence money, just as if it stood still — perhaps more because of the exposure to further delay. This cost must be charged against the route involved and compared with the cost of probable actual delay and with costs on competitive routes.

It will seldom be economic to dawdle for such reasons — hence the facts must be understood. This mental process typifies a popular rationale (not unique to railroads) that denies the existence of costs not directly visible.

Ownership costs exist in all industry, including railroading, and many of the problems of the industry arise from misunderstanding them. One characteristic of an integral train system is that its costs — including the dominant time costs — can be isolated, and another is that its students have been more sophisticated than conventional railroaders in estimating ownership costs. This is why some railroaders believe the integral train system originated the ownership cost concept. Incidentally, the dominance of time (mostly ownership) costs is characteristic of transportation trades.

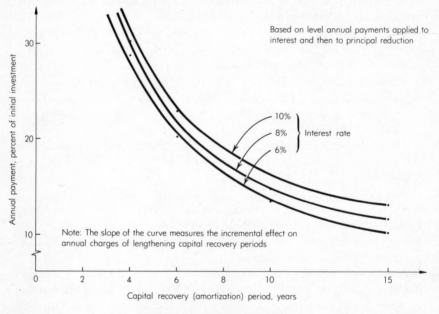

**3.1.1-A — Amortization Factors**

At usual interest rates, prolonging capital recovery beyond about 10 years no longer produces major reductions in annual capital recovery charges. Such prolongation does, however, increase the risk of obsolescence and increases total interest costs. Therefore few integral train systems will use capital recovery periods longer than about 10 years.

## 3.1.1 IATI

The initials mean "interest, amortization, taxes and insurance," all computed from the capital invested — defined as the total installed cost of anything required for an integral train system and not otherwise

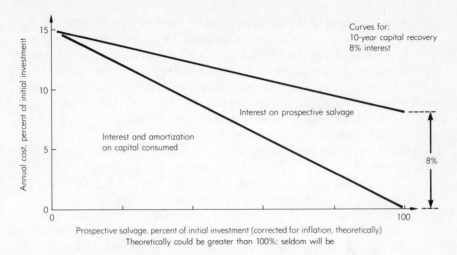

**3.1.1-B — Effect of Prospective Salvage on Capital Recovery Charges**

Obviously, where there is no prospective salvage, all the capital must be recovered during the amortization period. Also obviously, if an asset can be sold for what it cost, the transaction is simply a direct loan on which interest is paid. All other cases are intermediate.

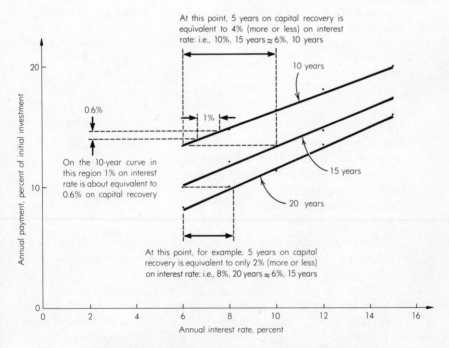

**3.1.1-C — Effect of Interest Rates on Capital Recovery Charges**

For any amortization period, increasing interest rates will call for increasing annual payments.

available — even if it is also used or to be used by other traffic. It excludes "sunk" costs which are not affected by integral train decisions. This rationale reflects the fact that a budget prepared to guide decisions is not concerned with anything the decision does not affect. Inclusion of IATI in a cost budget converts capital into annual cost, and it no longer makes any difference whose capital is used. The question "Whose capital?" is then answered "Whoever wants the interest money." Profit is not counted until all costs, including IATI, are met.

Interest, amortization, taxes and insurance are sometimes called finance costs or capital charges. They can be estimated thus:

The initial cost of an asset is estimated, including the non-recurring financing cost, design, installation, and all other costs of an in-place facility. A realistic amortization or capital recovery period is selected, never longer than the projected physical or useful life of the asset. The prospective salvage value at the end of the amortization period is then estimated and the rate of interest that must be paid on borrowed money is selected. This rate must not be confused with required rates of profit — interest is not profit; it is part of cost. The rate to be applied to cover taxes and insurance must then be estimated, and the computation goes this way (using a numerical example):

| | |
|---|---:|
| Initial cost | $743,000 |
| Interest during construction | |
| (8% per year for 6 months) | 30,000 |
| | 773,000 |
| Prospective salvage | 180,000 |
| Capital consumed | 593,000 |
| Interest and amortization (10-year capital | |
| recovery, 8% interest, level payments) | 89,000 |
| Interest on salvage at 8% | 14,000 |
| Taxes and insurance at 6% of | |
| initial investment | 47,000 |
| Total annual charge | $150,000 |

The interest and amortization figures (I&A) are recognizable as the cost of financing a level-payment bank loan. They provide equal annual payments covering interest and a payment on principal each year to pay back the portion of capital consumed — like a standard home mortgage. The salvage item is financed as if it were a "balloon note" on which interest must be paid each year until the proceeds of the salvage sale repay it. Inflation introduces a conservative bias when it exceeds estimates.

Taxes and insurance in this example are budgeted at a level rate, 6%

of the initial cost. This is about equal, on average, to 10% to 12% of
varying book value. Some assets will have higher and some will have
lower T&I charges. For example, a railroad embankment does not need
fire insurance, and some jurisdictions do not tax machinery.

The selection of the primary factors — capital recovery period and
interest rate — must be based on judgment. The annual interest and
capital recovery factor (in this example 15%) is then taken from an
interest table or chart.

When the annual capital charges are included in costs it no longer
makes any difference whose capital is used. However, profits remaining after these charges are met should not be referred to as return on
investment. This computation determines what must be paid to a bank
for money, just like paying for any other purchased commodity.

When a cash flow analysis is wanted, the I&A items can be added to
profits. This consideration is sometimes important when different kinds
of investment must be compared.

*For example:* Great Lakes iron ore movement requires
heavy inventories to permit use of seasonal shipping. Such investments are not subject to amortization but are "rolled over"
every year. Traditional thought asserts that these investments
are liquid when in fact the only way to make them liquid is to
liquidate the steel mill or ship year-round by a reliable means.
When the same money is invested in an integral train system
the cash position changes for the better. The iron ore is a long-
term capital requirement which must be renewed — at an in-
flated price — every year. The train commitment declines annually because its budget includes amortization money and its
salvage value rises with inflation.

## 3.1.2 Standby Time

**Variations of standby time occur in all service trades but are not al-
ways recognized. Time allowed for accident and mechanical failure
is the most easily recognized. Others include time waiting for crews,
for patron functions, and the like. This latter is *a* reason why economic
planning demands the logistics concept, with loading and unloading
included in the design unit — standby time can then be compared with
terminal costs when they are both in the same budget.**

Standby time and delay allowances — which have some of the same
characteristics — are elements of equipment time. They must be
charged for at the same rates as any other time. They must be considered in economic choices and they must be included in total budgets —
they *are* real costs.

It is usually salutary to itemize them in detail in presentations intended for managements. This practice tends to minimize the inclination to demand large allotments of standby time for the sake of operators' convenience — once it has a price tag and must be justified, the "need" for availability time tends to decline. If such discussions are not controlled they deteriorate until someone says, "It would be still better to stay home and get the check in the mail."

Part of a planner's task is to insist that such allotments be limited to time actually needed.

*For example:* One division had a daily passenger train whose schedule was quite unreliable — the superintendent had been running his remote division quite informally until his erratic performance attracted attention. He reported that an integral train would need 24 hours' standby time to get over his 88 miles (plus running time) — he had at least two and never more than five freight trains daily. His "reason" was that the rules required clearing the passenger's time and this might involve waits as long as 24 hours — the passenger had been known to be that late.

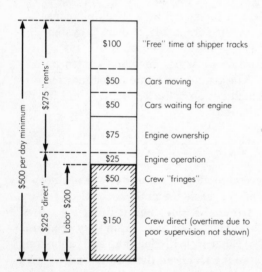

Traffic handled: Average 15 cars and associated empties; cost $30 to $35 each

### 3.1.2 — "Switcher" Costs

This cost distribution is that of a reasonably typical "peddler" in a dense industrial area. Characteristically, rentals amount to more than all other costs of terminaling. The local management, also typically, reported that the "cost" of this operation was $150 (crew direct labor) and applied to 30 cars — counting the empties — or $5 per car. This is obviously not the whole cost and it is also true that railroad cost men at "headquarters" would come closer. But it is important that many front-line management men carry this error into their decision-making.

### 3.1.3 Facility Costs

Facilities, defined as fixed plant, also have ownership costs whether railroad-owned or shipper-owned. They usually run with time and are usually independent of actual volume, once the facility is built. It is conservative to project short service lives, reflecting potential obsolescence.

> *For example:* A track built or bought for an integral train system should be amortized over the same 10-year period used for the trains despite the fact that most track is amortized over longer periods and can be made to last longer. It is then consistent to budget consumption-level maintenance and to design a short-life (fast amortization) facility.

IATI for facilities is computed in the same way as it is for trains. The previous sample IATI computation purposely contained no distinction between moving and fixed assets.

Some industrial economists profess to see a difference between these kinds of investment. Actually the security for even a car lease is the user's credit. This is precisely the security for a fixed plant lease or mortgage. A common theme on this subject claims to attach importance to the allegedly ready diversion of some kinds of assets to other uses. This argument is without much real substance but there are examples in the industrial world in which its use has persuaded industrial buyers to spend large sums of money with salesmen who use it.

> *For example:* A user with a known short-life use (a construction job) bought special cars on the vendor's assurance that they would be readily resold whereas the fixed plant alternate could not. They were not readily salable by virtue of being specials. This same user bought the costly fixed plant, *too*, but that is another story.

## 3.2 Other Time-Based Costs

Some time-based costs, besides ownership costs, run 8,760 hours a year, and others are referred to service hours. Crew labor is seldom time-based, nor is incidental labor such as signalmen. Continuous items often are, for calculating convenience, added to IATI and included in imputed rental.

> *For example:* The ICC demands locomotive "inspections" at fixed intervals regardless of mechanical needs. The resulting costs can be estimated on an hourly basis as a continuous cost that runs 8,760 hours a year.

Costs that are proportional to service hours or intensity of use include such things as fuel. Others are system costs unrelated to specific units.

*For example:* An integral train system's management and solicitation cost does not "belong" to individual trains and is not relevant to certain classes of operating decisions. It may be convenient but it is misleading to include it in train rent — doing so would distort such decisions as whether to wait or detour, for example, by overstating train time values. Such a choice based on artificially allocated "costs" is tantamount to claiming, for favored alternates, credit for "savings" that cannot actually be realized.

### 3.2.1 Inspection and Scheduled Maintenance

Most fixed and movable equipment maintenance will be regularly programmed. It happens that such a program is most easily budgeted, though this is not the reason for using it. Cars, power, conveyors, mobile equipment, etc., will be subject to mechanical inspection and repair at regular intervals and the resulting costs can be calculated (in terms of labor and materials) as an annual cost. When this is done, the time cost of a unit will include this cost for all time in service. In general, any choice that uses time will add units that will then demand this maintenance, so supporting the pertinent basic rationale.

*An exception* to this general procedure will occur in the case of small operations in which routine maintenance is done intermittently at an existing facility. In such cases maintenance and inspection costs are treated as event costs.

Locomotives will require monthly, quarterly, semiannual and annual inspections. Some types will also require major overhauls during their amortization periods — e.g., most diesels will need one "top deck job" during a 10- to 12-year amortization period.

For presently available and prospective locomotive types the cost of this work must be budgeted for an entire amortization period. A monthly inspection, for example, will involve some number of man-hours of labor and some amount of money for materials and supplies. The estimate will be made essentially in this form:

Hypothecate a 10-year amortization period. Each unit will need:

|  | Labor, man-hrs | Supplies $ |
|---|---|---|
| 9 annual inspections | xx | xx |
| 10 semiannual inspections | xx | xx |
| 20 quarterly inspections | xx | xx |
| 80 monthly inspections | xx | xx |
| 119 Totals | xxx | xxx |
| Times hourly rate | y | |
| | | xy |
| Total cost | | xxxx = C |

Annual cost is $\frac{C}{10}$ in dollars per year per unit

The numbers to be entered will depend on the kind of engine and its requirements. They are estimated by interviewing vendor and user staff and examining (but not using unthinkingly) available records — e.g., time slips, requisitions and vendors' sales material.

The "top deck job" in the case of diesels, or corresponding overhauls for other types of engines, should be estimated for the requirements during the amortization period — in this example for the first 10 years of the life of the machine.

This total, divided by the amortization period, is then an average annual cost of this function. "Long term" projections are not relevant — at the end of the amortization period a choice exists between using the now secondhand units and buying equipment then available.

A refinement, seldom justified, is to use a sinking-fund computation to make major overhaul money available when needed. The use of an "average" for what are largely deferred expenses is somewhat conservative, but anticipated inflation will consume some or all of the conservative bias introduced in this way.

Similar computations will be needed for cars but seldom for fixed plant because fixed plant utilizations will be very low — a design of which this is not true is probably not the most economic design. The unit cost of periodic maintenance for cars will be much lower than for engines because they are greatly less complex — but there are many more of them. Generally, cars will need semiannual attention, a small part of it demanded by regulatory agencies. Planners should budget more than the legally required minimum because it will be found economic to practice more preventive maintenance than has been traditional. Random inspections — s.o.p. in car work — are uneconomical; even worse, they are ineffectual.

Even with low-utility conventional cars, preventive maintenance would almost always be economically advantageous. However, the fact that cars in conventional railroading are "nobody's business" inhibits the practice of preventive maintenance by concealing the effects of the cost of *not* practicing it. Reflection on conventional wheelwork, weight stenciling, brakework, etc., will be informative.

Facilities will usually also require time-based maintenance. For example, driveways can be budgeted an annual cost for snow removal and pavement repairs.

However, most integral train terminals will be designed for low investments, low utilization (to keep the costly trains busy), and short lives. Therefore most of them will use relatively little maintenance during their amortization periods. Subsequent projections are immaterial to initial budgets.

This matter is related to busines philosophy. The integral train planner's attitude must be that if an installation repays its capital and pays a profit and then falls apart so that a new decision *must* be made, it has been a commercial success. Neither investments nor maintenance can often be justified merely on the basis of longevity — if for no other reason than because such outlays take unacceptably long to produce return — by definition.

### 3.2.2 Management, Solicitation and Supervision

Any business requires these services, and the integral train business is no exception. The amount of such service will vary from one case to another — from one man, part time, to a considerable force — and may vary during the life of the system. It should not be reduced to a unit charge in any way that will lead to the use of "burdened" rates in making design choices.

Costs in this category are best estimated in toto, and careful thought should be given to *any* proposal to allocate them. It will usually be necessary — for financing, rate and management presentations if for no other reason — to allocate such costs over tonnage for any diverse-purpose system. Allocations can be arbitrary in such cases or can be made to serve immediate purposes. For "private" systems it is usually advisable to report such costs as a system total unless there is a specific reason for suggesting an allocation basis.

Costs in this category can be budgeted in this form:

$/yr

Director or executive supervision
Office manager, "dispatcher" or 24-hr phone man
Clerical cost
Branch office managers
Branch office assistants
Main office rent and supplies
Branch office rent and supplies
Salesmen (where applicable), base or draw
and expenses (sales commissions, if paid, are
usually percentages of gross and are reported as
deduction from income)
Annual total                                           $

### 3.2.3 Fuel Cost

Fuel is often the second largest item in an integral train budget. Some engines have flat fuel rates over a considerable load range and others show wide rate/load variations. The practical way to estimate fuel consumption is to divide the trip or cycle into segments, each comprising a number of hours at some rate or load level. The total number of hours will be the trip or cycle total — including idling time. This last is important because there usually is a lot of it, and it is an obvious omission for a critic to find, even when it represents a small amount of money.

For the foreseeable future most engines will burn diesel oil — diesels and gas turbines as well. Long-term projections for gas turbine fuels apparently tend to liquified natural gas (LNG). However, the technological problems are considerable, and they will take a while to solve.

Quoted fuel cost for large volumes usually includes station tankage. This condition is likely to continue as long as the oil business is competitive — and in some cases the price of oil even includes putting it aboard the train. The business is attractive — a large integral train can take aboard upward of 10,000 bbl. at one time. It is also obvious that the integral train will not be bunkered from a tank wagon like a standard diesel unit. It will, though, sometimes be bunkered from a barge or tanker.

> *For example:* A bunkering facility can consist of a barge
> wharf, pump, trackside pipe and several hose connections —
> for occasional use; such a scheme is too slow to use often.

It will seldom, if ever, be economic to switch out the fuel cars and run them to a refinery. Such an operation is tantamount to using costly rolling stock for tankage, and the volumes are rarely high enough for an oil-carrying integral train. Fuel delivery to an integral train repair station can be by pipeline from a nearby refinery, but any commitment that inhibits open-market fuel buying should be closely examined.

The process of budgeting fuel consumption should proceed on a trip basis. The process is as follows:

> Estimate the *total* time in the round trip, including loading,
> unloading, terminal, service, and delay times.

> Divide the round trip into several segments of time, with
> due regard to speeds, load conditions, grades, and any other
> pertinent factors. Each such subdivision should be associated
> with a total-train (including spares) load level.

> Suggested load levels are:
> Idling or coasting
> >  10% of power (of total train)
> >  25% of power
> >  50% of power
> >  75% of power
> > 100% of power

The time at full load will be relatively small, and there will be a considerable amount of idling time. Most loading and unloading will use about 10% of the train's power. Running at full speed over *most* lines will use about 50% of the train's power.

It is possible to make a machine run, on those railroads that have computers and programs. Experience indicates that a reasonably competent estimator can reach conclusions that are adequate for the uses to which they are put, without recourse to the computer. Existing programs and arrays of constants devised for conventional trains may not be applicable or suitable for extrapolation to integral train applications, and caution is suggested.

The calculation is most easily arranged thus:

|  |  |  |  |  |
|---|---|---|---|---|
| _____hrs at idle | (_____gph) | = | | gal |
| _____hrs at 10% | (_____gph) | = | | |
| _____hrs at 25% | (_____gph) | = | | |
| _____hrs at 50% | (_____gph) | = | | |
| _____hrs at 75% | (_____gph) | = | | |
| _____hrs at 100% | (_____gph) | = | _____ | |
| Total | | | | x number of units in train |

_____

Total fuel used in one cycle          gal.

To avoid unnecessary use of large numbers the estimate should be made in terms of one engine unit, using whole-train percentages. For diesels it makes little difference in fuel consumption whether power levels are controlled by running at low loads or shutting down some units — there is a maintenance advantage in running all units at all times. For gas turbines the economic relationships are such that engines in use usually are best run at full load — and the fuel consumption is closely proportional to total train power output.

Total fuel consumption is then obtained by multiplying the total above obtained by the number of engines in the train. In-train spares should be included in all calculations, and load percentages should take due cognizance of them — this is another reason 100% load will seldom be used.

Fuel needed for car heat, where used, can be estimated by assuming 5 to 7 kilowatts per car for about 60% of the time that the train is operating in temperatures below 35° F. (when it returns empty) — with a thermal efficiency appropriate to the primary equipment used.

The total fuel cost can then be estimated in dollars per mission by applying pertinent fuel prices.

### 3.2.4  Miscellaneous Time-Based Costs

Some, such as basic track maintenance and snow removal, will be associated with facilities and others will relate to rolling equipment.

*For example:* A track used occasionally by an integral train and budgeted entirely to it — whether exclusively used by it or not — will cost about $2,500 per mile per year (1967) despite the fact that there will be years in which none of this money is used.

*For example:* A train will require unscheduled maintenance of some of its engines on some trips, and this cost must be estimated and allowed for whether it is used on every trip or not.

In finding the various miscellaneous items, there is no substitute for a thorough, knowledgeable man with an inquiring turn of mind. This subsection can list only a few of those more frequently encountered and caution that each project will contain some that are unique to it and unsuspected until found.

*Equipment*

Time for unscheduled maintenance outages

Time lost and direct cost of road failures leading to immobile equipment

Time lost and direct costs of repairs resulting from accidents

Repainting, stenciling and other marking

Testing and inspection by regulatory agencies, not related to need or productive work

Repairs to minor parts — e.g., hand brakes — and to legally demanded but unused parts — e.g., ladders

*Facilities*

Plowing snow and patching pavement

Initial track maintenance

Painting, relamping, lubrication and similar minor maintenance

Postage and telephone charges

Minor maintenance material

The total of these items and others will usually be small. Attention to detail is related to a need to produce convincing as well as correct results. Most estimators can provide a suitable blanket allowance for this group — neither unrealistically low nor extravagantly high. But too many people will not believe such a budget — including some who just do not want to believe.

Part of this rationale starts with the conviction that past costs just cannot be capable of improvement. When a man so convinced cannot challenge the listed costs he assumes that the "miscellaneous" just must be or should be large enough to lead to the total he wants to believe.

### 3.3 Train Crews

Considerable has been said about the waste of human resources involved in featherbedding. But most employees who featherbed are individuals whose usefulness elsewhere would be seriously questioned — which fact helps to project the realistic likelihood of improvement. Such men in their younger days have waited out working conditions that drove off the most resourceful and adaptable men. Therefore it is not realistic to expect any improvement in this area or to expect judgment, skill or accessory work, even of train crewmen with no assigned function.

Train design must accommodate the fact that an engineman can seldom be regularly assigned to integral trains, nor can he be expected to learn a special skill. Through runs, that could offer a normal number of hours of steady work to justify upgrading skills, will be frustrated by the parochial views of "ownership" found among the "running trades."

Integral train firemen and brakemen will have little or no function. It is not even realistic to expect them to operate the door pushbuttons, inspect for open doors or perform any specific tasks at all except to assist in setting off occasional cripples or to "stand by" while messages are passed by train phone or radio. Similarly, conductors will have few duties — there are no wheel reports, for example.

Pragmatism demands that existing labor contracts be taken as they are, anticipating no improvements and no regular, specific duties for any crewmen except the driver. Labor cost saving will be attained by eliminating whole functions — or merely avoiding high-cost routes — i.e., shortening the process.

> *For example:* If one route (e.g., any route across Minneapolis and Saint Paul) requires a transfer crew, it is a cost just like the cost of a steep hill. Route selection includes review of alternates. The planner seeks low cost, not "justice" for employees who erect toll gates or those whose routes are thereby penalized.

> *For example:* The whole problem of yards will not arise at all (except for transfer crews, which will often reduce simply to paying for a timecard, with no actual service rendered) because the train will not be yarded or classified.

> *For example:* One route's "chain gang" service will cost "normal" rates, and on another route assignments and "home" terminals will lead to double pay. The high-cost route does not get a share; it gets *none*.

Industrial forces will handle the train on industrial property. Mechanical service will be contracted directly by the train's owner, usually its user.

Labor variables are as important as grades, curves, miles, etc. Most managements have contracted away much of their right to manage, and many labor organizations that control operations do not understand the need to compete for business. The planner must be objective — and may thereby hasten abandonment of routes "owned" by men who demand unrealistic tolls. Education is usually outside the scope or budget of the integral train system planner.

### 3.3.1  Mileage-Basis Crews

A "normal" crew day is 100 miles — plus arbitraries — and subject to review with local supervision to find the peculiarities of each division or district (virtually all "local conditions" are "adders"). It is often convenient to apply the mileage rates (typical for "chain gang" and turn service) to an entire trip and then to add the arbitraries. In this context, planners must include "constructive mileage" — e.g., miles paid for but not run to make up minima, or imputed to certain functions which may or may not have real identities.

Wage rates must be reviewed with suitable officials of each railroad. They are part of the union contract, and few railroads are reluctant to discuss them. There usually is a scale for an entire system or each part of a system. Even on small systems there usually are also local conditions. If the recommended liaison procedure is followed, the system-level discussion will precede local discussions. Division superintendents and other local officials thus need not become involved in repetitious system data gathering. Local supervision is directly involved, though, in most of the arbitraries — there is no other reliable data source besides local supervision in this area. But what is told the researcher must be tested for correctness. One becomes a skeptic.

Train and engine crew wage rates are stated in variations of the following form:

Enginemen and firemen:
   A base rate per 100 miles for engines up to a stated minimum weight on drivers
   An increment, in terms of a rate per "day" for additional weight on drivers. Integral trains will usually be heavier than the tables published, but the curve is a straight line and the planner will use its formula.
Conductors and brakemen:
   A base rate per 100 miles for trains up to a minimum number of cars
   An increment, in terms of a rate per "day" for cars over the minimum
In nearly all cases there are rates for "local" and "through" service

which do not differ greatly. A planner must usually use the "local" rate where the train makes a delivery.

Nearly all road crew rates call for payment of miles, with a straight-line variation. Most also call for overtime if time exceeds miles (at 12.5 miles per hour). Routes that pay for time *and* miles will usually not be competitive.

Integral train schedules will seldom result in overtime, possibly except when the turn crew or through crew passes the train over a hopper or through a loader in road territory. In such cases where no "work" is done — i.e., no couplers are handled and no train employee gets off his chair — the total elapsed time will still often be less than the "equivalent" of the miles. Even then, it is probably advisable to budget the train crew for miles and for another day for passing the train over the hopper. Purely arbitrary, but the planner must be a realist, and a shipper on a more realistic line gets a commercial advantage.

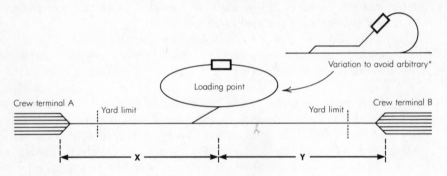

Pay basis, depending on local conditions, to run train A to loading point, around loop, and back:

1. 2x(minimum 100 miles) + arbitrary,* local rate, if total time is less than 2x/100 × 8 hours;

or 2. 2x(minimum 100 miles) + time on loop + arbitrary;*

or 3.. 2(x+y) + time on loop (minimum 8 hours) + arbitrary;*

or 4. 2(2x+y) + time on loop (minimum, maybe) + arbitrary* (if crews are "home" at B);

or other variations.

*Arbitrary varies, 2 hours to 8 hours, to change ends. (With loop shown it involves walking 100 feet, more or less)

### 3.3.1 — Loading or Unloading in "Road" Territory

This sketch will illustrate some of the bases encountered for estimating crew pay on the end segment of a cycle. The task performed is to take the train from the last crew terminal to a patron, pass it around the loop (or equivalent), and return it, in one continuous process, returning to the point of origin at the end of the task. The choice of pay basis depends entirely on the local rules and local contract provisions, which can be learned only by on-scene research.

The most useful procedure is to determine the "normal" day rate for a five-man crew. (No assumptions about crew size reduction should be made — supervision is such that there will always be a fireman "available" for the high-paying integral train even if the men next out have to mark off for other trains.) Then allowance for incidental wage-based costs must be made. This requirement has been steadily rising and for the next few years (1967) should be taken in the 30% to 35% range.

### 3.3.2 Time Basis Crews

Yard crews and others who spend long times moving short distances are paid time, usually with time and a half after 8 hours (or less). The traditional "8 within 10" has often become "10 within 8." Local crews, such as run a turn to load or unload, may be paid time when miles are too few to equal time spent, and in some cases are paid *both*. And sometimes both minima, too. Routes with excessively burdensome pay policies will seldom be competitive — and neither will shippers on those lines. Integral train economic rationale rejects cross-subsidization.

Road overtime will seldom occur in a properly supervised integral train operation. One of the advantages of the system is that it is less exposed to local crews who, essentially unsupervised, dawdle to assure overtime.

At the system wage-rate conference, time rates for time-paid crews will be obtained. Such rates usually are fixed in terms of a rate per 8-hour day (and sometimes guaranteed overtime) for each crewmember. There is usually also an increment for weight on drivers (for enginemen and firemen) and for cars more than a minimum (for conductors and brakemen). It is *not* economic to hold or extend train time to "use" the minimum day that must be paid for. Just because men are paid for time not worked does not justify paying for equipment not working.

The daily rate for a *five*-man crew must be computed for the train being used. No assumptions about productivity improvements are justified except when specifically supportable in particular situations. A minimum of 1 day will be budgeted for each crew. It is seldom economic to "borrow" a crew already on duty and pay only for time used.

When overtime is involved it must be estimated at time-and-a-half. It is usually advisable to plan on paying overtime if actual work is expected to exceed 6 hours in a shift. It is not often customary to expect work to start when the shift starts. Furthermore, some lines have arbitrary starting times. In such cases 6 hours, for example from 3 to 9 p.m., are likely to cost 2 "days."

When a train is delivered across town to another railroad, the crew of the delivering line will normally run to the receiving line's yard and return by taxicab. Such a crew will seldom be allowed, under existing agreements, to return another train. The crew will often seek and sometimes get still another "day" for traveling one way in a train and the other way in a taxicab — all within 8 hours or less — and there was one case in which crews tried for a "full crew" for the taxicab. (They did not get it.) There are instances in which work both ways is done in alternate months by each line's men. Such arrangements are of little value to integral train systems because of scheduling problems, but the arbitrary often agreed to when such arrangements were made will increase the cost of movement via such routes.

Time-basis crews are subject to the usual markup for wage-based incidentals, currently (1967) in the 30% to 35% range.

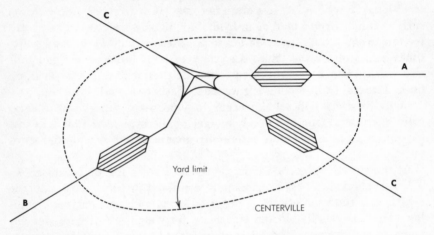

Railroad A to B or C ⎫
Railroad B to A or C ⎬ requires a "yard" crew and if not via yard also requires taxi
Railroad C to A or B ⎭ service (e.g., A or B to C or reverse without going to C's yard)
Railroad C, through, usually does not

Applicable railroad definitions are in terms of crew "ownerships," not carrier names

### 3.3.2 — Crosstown "Yard" Crew Conditions

The existence of a direct route or connection does not of itself establish that the cost of using it will be "normal" — even if present ownership is common. The matter depends on local labor agreements, and they in turn usually depend on long-forgotten original ownerships.

### 3.3.3  Arbitraries

The list is long and nonsystematic — this section can only illustrate. They can be budgeted only after knowledgeable conferences with local superintendents.

*For example:* On one railroad, hauling an extra caboose caused each crewmember to be paid an extra 1 cent a mile. On that line the integral train needs no caboose, but the crews are privileged to sleep in it at the end of the line — some just don't like the YMCA. So it must be attached to the integral train — at a switching cost — and its poor reliability impairs the schedule; or it must be sent on and the arbitrary paid.

Another common arbitrary is paid when an engineman must climb off one engine and get on another during his tour of duty.

This subsection can list only a few of the more common arbitraries. Discussion in depth with local supervision is the only practical way to find them all. One must merely endure the associated defensive reactions. A partial list is:

Reporting time, defined as an arbitrary time paid for, usually in addition to the day's pay, for coming to work.

"Dual service time," an arbitrary sometimes paid in addition to mileage and minima when travel is by two means of transportation — e.g., by taxi one way and by train the other way.

An arbitrary for riding on a locomotive not of railroad ownership.

An arbitrary for coupling air hoses and sometimes for not coupling them — and sometimes for *both*.

Riding in a locomotive cab instead of a caboose (for conductors and brakemen).

Use of telephones or train radios.

This writer's experience has been that *most* superintendents know what arbitraries apply on their own divisions, but that "system," "district," or "regional" officials are not a productive source of information in this respect. Experience shows, though, that superintendent-level conferences must capture the real interest of the men involved if the information obtained is to be complete and correct. Deliberate prevarication, even by the most dedicated foot-dragger, is rare though not entirely unheard of.

### 3.3.4 Deadheading

Commonly one end of a division is "home," even when employees live at the opposite end. Such men are paid for "working" over the division when a trip starts or ends elsewhere than at "home," under some conditions, whether they actually travel or not. It is seldom practical to change such a condition. It will often develop that the resulting double crew pay is the only substantive difference between competing routes — in which case the high-cost route gets no business.

Deadheading, whether actually performed or not, is paid for at contract rates, and these rates must be determined on each property. There are two variations and for most integral trains there is a large difference:

A — Paid at the rate that applies to the train.

B — Paid at a "base" rate.

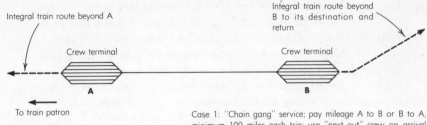

Integral train route beyond A

Integral train route beyond B to its destination and return

Crew terminal

Crew terminal

**A**

**B**

To train patron

Case 1: "Chain gang" service; pay mileage A to B or B to A, minimum 100 miles each trip; use "next out" crew on arrival

Case 2: "Home" at A, train time (round trip) beyond B more than 8, less than 16 hours; pay mileage A to B and B to A, minimum 100 miles, each way, each round trip; hold crew at B and provide accommodations

Case 3: "Home" at A, time beyond B more than 16 hours; pay A to B and B to A each trip each way; or pay A to B, + time from 16 hours to resumption of duty ( + B to A, regardless of total actual time, sometimes subject to minimum)

Case 4: "Home" at B; pay B to A deadhead, A to B working, B to A working, A to B deadhead, each round trip

When most present operation uses "assigned" crews there is no "chain gang" or pool of crews awaiting work at the "far" end. Some dense integral train services can use their own "assigned" crews from the local roster

### 3.3.4-A — Road Crew Conditions

The crew cost of moving an integral train one round trip over an intermediate division (not containing either end of the run) can vary widely with local labor agreements and conditions. This sketch illustrates some of the variables involved.

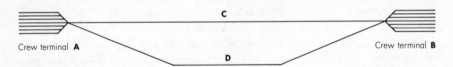

**C**

Crew terminal **A**

Crew terminal **B**

**D**

When A-C-B is not in the same crew "ownership" as A-D-B (e.g., different present or long-extinct underlying companies), then a round trip A-D-B-C-A costs (in crew wages): A-D-B working and deadhead back plus B-C-A working and deadhead back

### 3.3.4-B — Diverse Routing

Diverse routing usually costs double in crew labor, even when the railroad names on both routes are the same. Local inquiry is necessary. This condition does not necessarily apply when alternate *round trips* use the two routes. It usually does apply when an attempt is made to convert the two routes into "one-way streets" for efficient train-running unless a "paired track" agreement has been negotiated, and in that case an arbitrary payment usually was agreed to.

Which condition exists is established in the wage-rate conference, and practices are not uniform among railroads. When condition B exists the applicable rate must be obtained from the railroad's labor relations office.

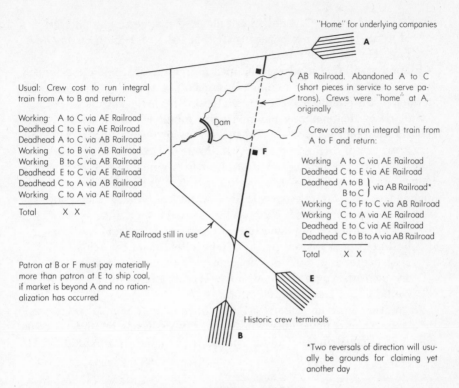

"Home" for underlying companies

**A**

Usual: Crew cost to run integral train from A to B and return:

AB Railroad. Abandoned A to C (short pieces in service to serve patrons). Crews were "home" at A, originally

Working   A to C via AE Railroad
Deadhead C to E via AE Railroad
Deadhead C to A via AB Railroad
Working   C to B via AB Railroad
Working   B to C via AB Railroad
Deadhead E to C via AE Railroad
Deadhead C to A via AB Railroad
Working   C to A via AE Railroad
_____
Total      X  X

Dam

Crew cost to run integral train from A to F and return:

**F**

Working   A to C via AE Railroad
Deadhead C to E via AE Railroad
Deadhead A to B } via AB Railroad*
                B to C }
Working   C to F to C via AB Railroad
Working   C to A via AE Railroad
Deadhead E to C via AE Railroad
Deadhead C to B to A via AB Railroad
_____
Total      X  X

AE Railroad still in use

**C**

Patron at B or F must pay materially more than patron at E to ship coal, if market is beyond A and no rationalization has occurred

**E**

**B**

Historic crew terminals

*Two reversals of direction will usually be grounds for claiming yet another day

### 3.3.4-C — An "Orphaned" Line

Conditions like this arise when some long-gone management took a path of least resistance in negotiating a "settlement" — and there are some amazing examples extant. In one case a 10-mile remnant "belongs" to a seniority list consisting of one crew which is paid *five* days for each time a passing road crew enters the branch — and this crew does no actual work at all. Here, too, local inquiry is essential. The usual treatment is to buy the coal somewhere else.

Deadheading pay applies when a crew is taken by any means of transportation to the opposite end of a division to board a train or is taken "home" after delivering the train to the far end. It is ordinarily not paid when "chain gang" service or first-in-first-out conditions prevail, nor is it ordinarily used when a crew runs a turn to a point short of the distant (crew) terminal and returns to the starting point. When "chain gang" service is in use, an integral train may unbalance crews or it may tend to improve existing unbalance conditions. Local supervisors will nearly always assert that the integral train will unbalance crews. Researchers must verify such claims — they are seldom supportable in full as claimed, even when no overstatement was intended.

Deadheading is paid when a crew is taken by taxi to a junction or elsewhere to board a train. In such cases a combination rate lower than the full train rate for all travel may be applicable, though there may also be an arbitrary.

*For example:* One negotiator claimed that getting in and out of a taxicab was a separate craft that called for another day's pay. He got an arbitrary.

Planners will find it advisable, until individuals become experienced, to return to the railroad's labor relations office to verify their determinations — the conditions are not related in any logical system.

Surprising deadheading payments are found when there have been several underlier companies, and successors in "ownership" to the long-forgotten original runs remain in the form of isolated bits of railroad. Some patrons are located on short branches which are remnants of a long route whose "home" is many miles away. Integral train service to such patrons is usually economically impractical because they could not survive in their markets if charged the needed crew costs.

*For example:* A power dam interrupted a line and the dam-building agency connected it to a parallel line of the same current ownership, but the "foreign" crews never obtained the "right" to run over the new route. It costs 9 crew-days to run a round trip of less than 100 miles.

At another junction where original lines of two companies crossed, the present traffic flows over what were two railroads in 1895. It costs about 250 "constructive" miles in addition to the approximately 110

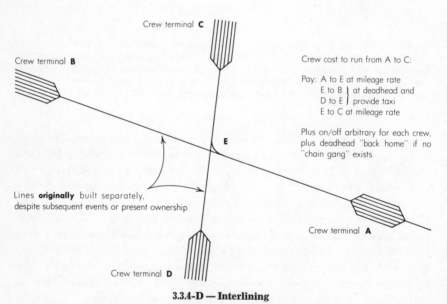

Crew terminal **C**

Crew terminal **B**

Crew cost to run from A to C:

Pay: A to E at mileage rate
    E to B ⎫ at deadhead and
    D to E ⎭ provide taxi
    E to C at mileage rate

Plus on/off arbitrary for each crew, plus deadhead "back home" if no "chain gang" exists

**E**

Lines **originally** built separately, despite subsequent events or present ownership

Crew terminal **A**

Crew terminal **D**

**3.3.4-D — Interlining**

When it is proposed to run via two railroads — even when they have the same names — researchers must watch for conditions like this one. It will still sometimes be economic to run the integral train on the interline route, but the cost cannot be estimated without local information.

actual miles of crew pay to move a train. Conventional service runs the engines the way they ran in 1895 and spends car and switching time at the "interchange." A shipper-planned integral train merely uses another railroad.

Researchers must remember that, in concept, train crews are not hired "to drive trains on the XYZ RR." but to "run trains between A and B," which stations on an original line may no longer be recognizable. These practices deny all facts of change for many years, and no improvement can realistically be forecast.

### 3.3.5—Selected Crew Terminal Costs

"Alimony" is paid to crews held away from "home" more than 16 hours — the theory is that a crew is entitled to a return run to be completed within 24 hours of arrival. It is paid under most contracts even if the crew gets 8 hours' pay in fewer hours returning, all completed in less than 24 overall hours. Furthermore, the 16 hours start on arrival, not at the end of the time already paid for.

Another crew terminal cost is I&FTD — initial and final terminal delay. The theory is that such delays might force men to put in as much as 8 hours for a day's pay. Thus a crew cannot be called too far in advance of train arrival, even when the *total* time on duty is less than that paid for.

Planners will use ingenuity to avoid such costs. Railroads will usually try to charge the integral train a "share" of average such costs for a division or district even when the integral train planner can avoid actually incurring any or can even reduce the costs incurred by other services. If it seems like a child's game with arbitrary rules, so be it. Planners must "play the game" the way it is.

In the case of "alimony," if a crew is held for 17 hours and then "works" 4 hours to "earn" 8, it will expect to be paid for 1 hour of alimony (sometimes subject to a minimum) and a day (or more) for the 4 hours of work. Similarly, if the crew is called after 16 hours to avoid the "alimony" and is then required to wait 1 hour and "work" 4, the pay will be more than 1 day — the 1 hour is initial terminal delay.

Supervision is needed to control final terminal delay. The crew will arrive in a locally defined terminal area and then can, if inadequately supervised, dawdle en route to the stopping point to "earn" final terminal delay. This matter will also be pertinent to the provision of taxi service — waiting for the cab will be paid for as an extra even when the total time on duty is less than paid for. Similarly, a road crew can dawdle if inadequately supervised so that a crew of fellow employees, already called, can obtain ITD.

Most railroads find that this group of costs is expensive. Most supervisors try to bury them in averages and want the integral train to assume a "share." This is in part a concern with obtaining as much money as possible — review the rationale of divisions. But it is, in part, an attempt to protect an intellectual position that has developed — and has been inherited — over years of sloppy supervision and inept — sometimes "lame duck" — labor negotiations. The presence on the line of a train that does not incur these costs in large amounts is an embarrassment — supervisors will be expected to do as well with other trains, they fear.

It happens to be true that the conditions imposed usually make it impractical for conventional trains to achieve integral trains' low costs. This family of costs is one of the places where that condition is prominently manifested. Top-level managers may not see the inherent advantages of integral trains, and hence local supervisors may believe — with some justification — that their own seniors will be among those who do not see them. Hence the defensive attitudes. A local man fears the integral train lest it "give his boss ideas." The planner must continually try to educate.

### 3.3.6 Miscellaneous Crew Cost Conditions

**A few miscellaneous conditions are reviewed, primarily to alert planners to the need to search for and evaluate a wide variety of unsuspected debits and credits.**

> *For example:* **An integral train may be coupled ahead of another train or can deadhead an engine (on its rear end) that must move anyway, and its crew cost, properly, should be shared in such cases.**

An integral train can pull cars that do not belong to it, thus performing a service for which some credit should be allowed. Any such schemes should be carefully analyzed, but some will survive analysis. (Mechanical reliability of the conventional equipment and time to attach it are important elements.)

In other cases an integral train can actually reduce some existing labor costs for other trains.

> *For example:* An integral train system may add enough traffic volume to permit the use of an assigned service or to reduce traffic intervals so that less "alimony" is paid to "chain gang" crews.

It will rarely, if ever, be proposed that the labor contract be changed or opened to negotiations. As a rule of thumb — if on any line some matter *must* be negotiated — a shipper-planned integral train system will usually use some other route.

Planners will find it practical to avoid most controversial items and

budget their own costs — and not claiming credits introduces conservative bias as well as relative peace and quiet. It is usually the part of
wisdom to leave the peripheral savings for the railroad to find for itself
— though "guidance" may be needed.

## 3.4  Trip and Event Costs

**These costs are discontinuous with respect to time, distance, and vol-
ume. The estimator must examine the operation and list the tasks
needed — in detail — and then estimate the costs of each. To do so he
must choose a way to do each task. The engineering function is to find
ways of avoiding as many of them as possible and then to perform the
remainder at minimum cost. No labor productivity improvement can
be expected, and no coordination with other railroad functions should
be relied upon.**

The need for thoroughness is obvious — to avoid embarrassing, even
if trivial, omissions. It is inappropriate to use historic or general experience which, by including entrenched nonessentials, overstates attainable costs. As is the case in building estimating, detailed estimates
are needed to develop reliable totals of items about which little is
known. The variety is wide, and no book can anticipate them all. The
estimator must therefore list the functions for each trip or cycle and
must be thorough as well as of an inquiring turn of mind.

These costs, mostly independent of train size, tend to weight choices
toward larger trains.

### 3.4.1  Tolls and Arbitraries

**These small items do not justify much effort to secure great precision.
They must be listed in detail to fend off nit-picking but can be estimated
generously. They include both fixed and variable costs — e.g., track-
age-rights operations shared on a "wheelage" basis, bridge tolls, facility
rents, and the like.**

The best that can be done here is to list some of them and to caution
planners to be thorough in their discussions with local railroaders, and
to draw on their own fund of experience. Such a partial list is:

Bridge tolls
Joint facility rents — e.g., track through a union station
Loading terminal labor
Towermen, switch tenders, etc.
Supervisors assigned to "hand hold" the train
Inspectors for the "500-mile" inspection

Exclusions that may require discussion include
Towermen and switch tenders, on duty for other purposes, who
may handle the integral train

Supervisors regularly on duty, in whose territory the integral
train moves

Inspectors and similar functionaries who do not work on the
integral train

Joint facility rents that are not affected by additional traffic,
depending on local agreements

Some labor is available at no cost, but planners will seldom win this
controversy, correctness or no.

> *For example:* One railroad has an "attrition" agreement and
> is paying towermen and others for no duties to maintain guar-
> anteed employment levels. It would seem that such a man
> would be available for duties in his "trade" occasionally. Plan-
> ners would do well to assume that such men would want an-
> other day's pay if they have to work at the employment they
> have been guaranteed.

One often-found family of problems arises in estimating "wheelage"
charges when joint costs are allocated on the basis of number of cars.

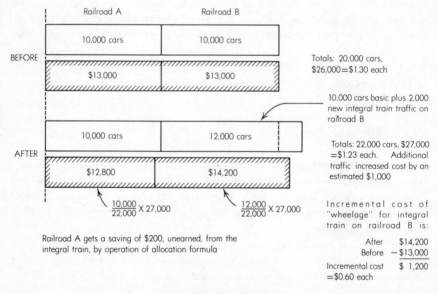

Railroad A gets a saving of $200, unearned, from the
integral train, by operation of allocation formula

### 3.4.1 — Wheelage Charges

Joint facility costs are often apportioned among railroads on the basis of the number
of cars transited by each. Adding an integral train (or any other traffic) increases total
traffic, but total costs seldom increase in proportion to traffic volume. If precision is
warranted, it is necessary to estimate actual outlays and derive incremental effects by
comparing "before" and "after" figures. Many people called on to furnish data will seek
to attribute as much cost as possible to the integral train for obvious commercial and
philosophical reasons. Planners must examine such claims for their credibility. The
unwarranted burden usually must simply be borne.

This problem is made more complicated by the fact that several variables are beyond direct control:

A — Totals are paid as spent, usually with little budgetary control

B — The total traffic on which division is based varies with the fortunes of the railroad used *and* of other railoads as well

C — The integral train itself can expand the traffic base and so reduce the per-car charge

In estimating such costs the most promising procedure is:

Examine past expenditures to project total outlays, with due cognizance of volume changes

Examine traffic volume on each participating road and project future distribution

Estimate total and per-car charges with and without the integral train

Compare the payment exacted of the subject line in total with and without the integral train, to estimate the differential effect of the integral train

### 3.4.2 Dispatching, Coordination, Etc.

It is sometimes advisable to assign a man to guide a movement through a congested area. His efforts cost a day's wages and expenses — justified by train time saved. Where labor agreements fix the number of such men as telegraphers who will be paid, the actual incremental cost of a block operator, for example, for a day is often zero, though it will seldom be practical to get this point across in negotiations.

The usual cost for a supervisor or hourly man for a 1-day assignment, including "fringes" and the use of an automobile, is about $50 (1967). Though an integral train will require only a few hours of his time, he should be budgeted for a full day. His cost is justified if he can save only a few minutes of the time of an integral train.

Representative instances are:

Where a train must be closely supervised, or where other engines working in the neighborhood must be coordinated to pass the train promptly, a supervisor should be detailed to cover the movement.

Where two railroads must collaborate in congested territory, each may detail a supervisor to monitor the movement.

Where there is considerable street traffic and an integral train must make a delivery, it may be advisable to detail a traffic policeman.

Where it is advisable to load or unload occasionally on a main line, a 1-day block operator can be employed to pass trains around the integral train just like they might be passed around a work train. Accessory work in such cases can include switch tenders, who may be mechanized or not, depending on frequency of use.

### 3.4.3 Inspections

There are two types:
A — Functionally needed inspections
B — Purely formal inspections demanded by regulators
Both represent costs, but the choice of procedure and pay level of help used will vary between them.

Functionally needed inspections include:
Inspections at loading points (e.g., for open doors)
Trip inspection after unloading, primarily for mechanical work
Loaded car inspection for container trains

The station employee at bulk loading stations who tends the belt should see that doors are closed and the car is empty just before loading. Cars in sophisticated systems will be equipped with fail-safe closed-door circuits (using limit switches) and indicator lights. The observer should be above the car to see into it ahead of the loading point — to divert or interrupt material flow if a defective car appears, leaving the empty car in the train.

Each subsystem will be inspected at the service station, at a central point where trains pass, preferably empty, on each cycle. Subsystems will contain suitable check circuits and counters to facilitate inspection. Key parts will be examined for premature wear and malfunction, and any elements that are due on schedule will be changed out. Examining doors, couplers, and other mechanical parts for function and impending need for changeout is a task for qualified specialists, not routine car inspectors.

Container train systems require the containers to be locked down, and an inspector must verify that each such lock is engaged. Alternatively, locks can be equipped with limit switches and a closed-circuit pilot-light system. Such a system can be justified only in sophisticated operations.

Inspection must be planned and budgeted for each system at the trip-service station. There is now no "standard" system — technology is changing, and each design represents some advance over what went before. Therefore each labor requirement must be figured for itself. Planners are cautioned to avoid overdesign, either in labor budgets or in using more automation than can be supported on an incremental cost basis.

For the foreseeable future, computerized or complex systems are not warranted for inspection and maintenance control.

Purely nominal inspections are made at interchanges and at 500-mile intervals. For some reason best known to regulators, an "inspection" is needed when the train is relayed from one railroad to another, but if the railroads subsequently merge this inspection can sometimes be eliminated. It is "needed" if the subsidiary keeps its name — e.g., from the P&LE to the NYC — but it is not needed if the component lines lose their names.

Such formal inspections have little or nothing to do with function and can be carried out by any employee who pays dues to the union that "owns" the "job" — the principal task being to avoid delaying the train. They can be budgeted at $50 for a man and an auto. If he only puts in a timecard and does nothing, the train will not be delayed. An effective maintenance program needs experts — which roadside inspectors are not — and leaves very little for them to find.

### 3.4.4 Low-Volume Maintenance

**Facility components used at low intensity may incur no maintenance at all during their amortization period. It is often advantageous to amortize quickly, during a no-maintenance period, and then make a repair-or-replace decision. It is correct to budget no maintenance under such conditions but it is usually not practical to get the idea across. It is usually advisable to budget nominal maintenance to make the budget believable to the unsophisticated.**

One example of "legitimate" low-volume maintenance is found in track. A railroad track needs some maintenance even if traffic is zero. At very low volumes it makes no money difference whether the track is used or not — the incremental track maintenance cost of the first few trains is actually zero.

Conveyors will not need belt replacement until some substantial number of service hours are accumulated. At the utilizations that characterize integral train facility train service belts, this need is unlikely to arise until after the amortization period. Similarly, motors, idlers, chutes, etc., will survive their amortization periods without replacement or serious repair. Light, simple, even primitive and inexpensive, components should usually be selected to exploit this condition.

It is usually advisable to budget a nominal sum, often 1 percent of initial cost, solely to avoid controversy, when no actual outlays are expected to arise and design has been directed to secure this objective. Such a budget item is usually called a maintenance allowance, and an accompanying note should point out its nature and intent.

Incidentally, one reason for budgeting equipment that should need no maintenance is a distrust of and distaste for the problem of securing reliable service, plus the exposure to inflation involved in continuing service commitments with material labor content.

### 3.5 Noncrew Mileage Costs

**Popular thought relates transportation costs to miles, but integral train mileage-based costs are relatively small. The large time-based costs usually govern route selection — and most other choices that make up the design process.**

The track is the only important shared facility in most integral train programs and thus it is one around which considerable cost controversy can revolve. Track cost is small, and a planner can afford to be generous — but he will have to conduct a seminar in the definition of incremental cost. In this context the initial cost of keeping a track in service is a fixed cost. In some cases lightly used tracks over which an integral train occasionally runs will have no incremental maintenance, but planners are advised to budget as if this were not the case.

Many elements of railroad cost traditionally referred to train-miles are actually not so related.

*For example:* Many railroads figure such costs as painting stations, maintaining signals, plowing snow, and burning weeds in cents per train-mile. In a famous case involving subsidy for a suburban service the railroad claimed that twice as many trains, each half as long, doubled the cost of painting stations. Their accounts cited "system" figures to "prove" their point.

### 3.5.1 Incremental Track Cost

**Track built or retained for an integral train system is budgeted entirely to it, regardless of other uses for it. Shared track — e.g., main lines — will incur *incremental* maintenance in proportion to gross ton-miles at a rate to reflect track and equipment characteristics. It is seldom economic to upgrade track or improve maintenance standards for an integral train — only when time savings can support the change.**

Treatment of the cost of track built for an integral train can be illustrated with an example from this writer's experience. A large integral train system required about 40 miles of passing sidings — four long sidings — on one 700-mile region. Once built it is likely that other trains would use them, too. But they were budgeted as follows:

A — Initial cost, 40 miles of track in the locations chosen, of construction standards suitable to the integral train's needs — e.g., no signals

B — Initial cost, eight turnouts and spring rods, chosen for the convenience of the integral train — e.g., long, high-speed turnouts

C — IATI on these items was budgeted in full

D — Initial maintenance on this track was budgeted

E — The passage of each integral train over the line was charged incremental maintenance regardless of which track it used

The railroad was advised that if it elected to run other trains over the integral train system's track, that would not affect the integral train budget, but that if these other trains required accessories, such as signals, any resulting costs must be budgeted to the service that required them.

Incremental track maintenance can be estimated most readily in terms of total ton-miles. Such estimates differ from usual track maintenance estimates in several respects.

Integral trains are designed — even the least sophisticated of them — to reduce track maintenance. Big wheels, low-pow-

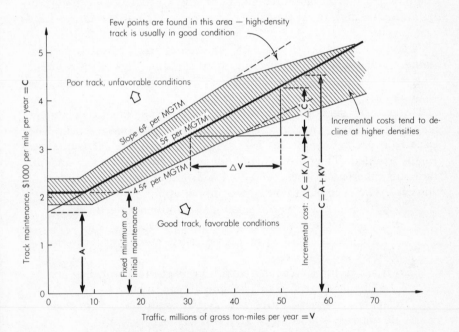

#### 3.5.1 — Track Maintenance Incremental Costs

For estimating the amount of additional money that should be assigned to a track maintenance function upon adding an integral train, it is the slope of the curve that is pertinent. This chart reports the findings of a study of actual experience in many places, adjusted for deferments of maintenance and other distorting elements. When an integral train system is substituted for conventional carriage, track maintenance cost is usually reduced. The total track maintenance item is so small that small differences in it seldom justify extensive discussion — especially so since credit for cost reductions is unlikely to be admitted. This chart reports experience with conventional operations and thus probably overstates costs for integral trains, so introducing a conservative bias.

ered (nonslip) driving axles, better brakes, no dragging equipment and the like will all operate to reduce track damage.

Average, past or "experience" costs on any railroad system are not relevant to this problem because both equipment and operating procedures differ from traditional.

Incremental costs are sought and by definition are less than "average."

Actual expenditures in any year are not relevant to the problem.

Reference is made to the basic definition of an incremental cost. Such a cost is a cost incurred if the traffic is moved *in the manner designed* and which would not be incurred if it were not moved. It is computed for the purposes of (a) choosing among alternate procedures and (b) reimbursing the actual incremental costs on a rational basis before negotiating the division of funds available for contributions to overheads and profits.

The appended chart shows a distribution of track maintenance data gathered over a period of time, in many situations, on many railroads. The costs are those generally of the 1963-1967 period and are subject to inflation.

These costs generally represent what division engineers thought should have been spent or sought to spend to maintain a track. They usually represent what was asked for, not what budget committees finally granted. They are adjusted for maintenance deferrals and subsequently increased work. They exclude some items not relevant to the case. For example, these figures do not apply:

To systems of track where pavement maintenance is unusually high — integral trains seldom go such places.

To yard tracks — either at high-density hump yards or neglected minor yards.

To track in unusually bad condition, neglected branches and the like — integral trains seldom go such places.

To signals, bridge painting, and special conditions where costs do not vary significantly with traffic.

Factors to be used must be selected for the kind of track involved. Main lines will be near the low side of the band and lesser lines will usually be near the high side of the band because lesser lines are normally maintained at lower standards. The unit incremental track maintenance cost is the *slope* of the curve.

For an empty-return bulk train, the computation can be shortened thus:

$$Cm = \frac{(Wg + Wt) \times C \times L}{100}$$

where Cm = incremental track maintenance cost in dollars per
round trip

Wg = gross or loaded weight, in tons

Wt = empty or tare weight, in tons

C = selected unit cost, in cents per thousand ton-miles

L = one-way line length in thousands of miles

The resulting estimate includes rail repairs, surfacing, ballast clean-
ing, normal crossing maintenance, and other ordinary trackwork. The
estimate may not apply in any one year since some work — e.g., rail
replacement — is done only at long intervals.

This estimate can be characterized as the amount of money
that the integral train system should give the division engineer
for his track budget every time it makes a trip, to make up
just what its passage costs, on a long-term basis.

### 3.5.2  Wheels, Axles, and Bearings

Car wheels — usually one-wear wheels — in integral train service
wear approximately in proportion to distance and are budgeted in
terms of total cost per wheel cycle — including interest. Locomotive
wheels are usually multiple-wear wheels and a cycle includes one or
more intermediate servicings. Lives are longer than in conventional service because service conditions can be controlled. Axles and bearings
— and their inspection and replacement — are budgeted in terms of
wheel cycles.

Car wheels, for sophisticated systems, will usually be one-wear
wheels of large diameter. Estimating procedure is:

Estimate wheel life. Large cast-steel wheels in integral train
service should last 150,000 to 250,000 miles, with the larger
figure associated with 45-inch wheels at 65,000 pounds per
axle.

Determine wheel cost (from manufacturers' quotations) and
estimate scrap value of worn wheels.

Estimate labor and other costs to remove and remount wheels
and bearings.

Schedule bearing inspection when wheels are removed. Roller
or cartridge bearings will normally survive two or three sets
of wheels.

Schedule axle inspection, using magnetic or similar methods to
find incipient failures. Most axles will survive longer than
the car — it is conservative to plan 2% axle replacement at
each wheel cycle.

Prepare the estimate thus:

| | | |
|---|---|---|
| Price of wheel | xx | |
| Scrap | —xx | |
| Net | xx | |
| Interest, 8% per year on original cost | xx | (1 year ±) |
| Labor to dismount and remount | xx | |
| Bearing inspection labor | xx | (one bearing) |
| Bearing replacement, about 40% of the price of *one* bearing | xx | |
| 50% of cost of inspecting axle | xx | |
| 50% of 2% of cost of replacement axle, net of salvage | xx | |
| Total | xxx | |

This total, multiplied by 8 and divided by wheel life in miles, yields a car-mile cost. It is multiplied by the number of non-motored cars in the train to yield a train-mile trailer wheel cost projection.

Locomotive or powered car wheels are usually multiple-wear wheels and their life is usually limited to about 200,000 miles with two intermediate trips to the wheel grinder. Their cost is estimated in the same way, for one wheel cycle. The computation can be carried out for single pairs or for locomotive sets.

In budgeting wheels and similar costs, care should be taken to avoid including plant and shop costs twice. Sophisticated systems will use their own shops, and such things as a wheel press and wheel grinder will be included in the shop budget. If, then, railroad experience costs are used to establish, for example, the cost of turning wheels, the computation includes the machines twice.

This point is intellectually related to similar observations elsewhere. Integral train budgeting must be carried out as a coherent whole. Shortcuts that use carrier past experience usually lead to overestimating. It is noteworthy that such conditions have contributed to carrier budgeting limitations in the past and thus to the need for integral train studies.

In estimating wheel costs for large systems it is usually advisable to separate the budget for the shop and its equipment as a system cost. Labor and supplies can then be estimated for each operation involved. This system produces consistent results when it is proposed to add trains to the system, to examine the influence of variations in volume, or to examine choices between private and shared facilities — rental of shared facilities is related to the cost of *owning* but not directly to the cost of *using* private facilities.

In the area of wheels and their accessories the only items of consequence not covered elsewhere are brake shoes. They are changed out on an inspection basis (but budgeted on a mileage basis) in connection with trip service. Long-life composition shoes will be virtually standard, especially on heavy cars of new design where they permit avoiding clasp brakes.

### 3.5.3 Other Mileage-Related Costs

**Many functions commonly thought of in terms of train-miles are actually fixed costs in the context of most integral train systems. This subsection is intended to note some of them and caution planners in their treatment.**

This section lists several kinds of costs that carrier cost men ordinarily list or report in terms of train-miles but which are not properly included in incremental cost budgets. The reasons for their exclusion are apparent. This is not to say that these costs need not be met. But they do not enter into choices among alternatives — including solicitation vs. nonsolicitation — and thus are not properly included in incremental costs. They are among the costs that are met out of the excess of revenues over incremental costs.

Signal maintenance

Real estate taxes on shared parts of the railroad

Painting and other maintenance of buildings and bridges not
exclusively used by or built for integral trains

Plowing snow and burning weeds

Repairing drainage structures on shared track

Wages of towermen and dispatchers required for all traffic

*For example:* One uninformed carrier man insisted that to
get even one more train over his road would require an entire staff of telegraphers and so no further traffic increments
should be solicited. The sales vice-president overruled him.

### 3.6 Volume-Related and System Costs

**Few costs actually vary with volume, but several "system" costs are "fixed" within an integral train system.**

*For example:* **Terminal ownership cost is a function of design volume but thereafter it is independent of actual volume. The minor cost of energy to run its conveyors is related to actual volume handled, and labor cost is related to number of trains handled.**

Several shippers' and receivers' peripheral costs are affected by volume. An integral train system can reduce most of these costs, and an integral train study should evaluate these savings — they are proper credits for the system regardless of what is done with the money.

One example of this group is inventory cost. The uninformed assume that an integral train system — because it uses big units — imposes inventory requirements that must be charged against it. Most integral train systems permit *reductions* in inventory, which should be credited. An extreme example is the Great Lakes ore movement, in which immediate capital credits (from liquidating inventory the integral train system makes unnecessary) exceed the new capital needed and the Lakers exist on mental inertia alone.

### 3.6.1 Terminal Charges

Terminal ownership cost is fixed when its capital cost is known, once a terminal is designed for a specific set of conditions — volume, frequency, etc. Its (small) operation and maintenance cost will vary directly with volume and inversely with train size (but not linearly). For example, a large train will seldom increase the per-trip operating cost, but more frequent calls will raise the annual operating costs. Even within this framework, however, costs will rise, for example, when a train size is reached at which it requires a second shift of station help.

The principal variable in terminal design is the rate at which an integral train is loaded or unloaded. Once a facility is built, additional traffic is usually handled at least cost by increasing the size of the train (if surge pile height permits) and not by buying more trains. Even when new belts are needed, this relationship is usually still valid. The relationship among the variables is illustrated thus:

The cost of electric energy required to unload a ton of bulk is usually less than 1 cent — mostly in the conveyor used to elevate the material to the top of the surge pile.

If the station uses two men, one highly skilled and one helper, the total employment cost will be less than $150, or less than 1 cent per ton for a small (15,000-ton) train or 0.5 cent per ton for a 30,000-ton train.

Train time will usually cost three times the station labor, often more.

If the station were designed originally for a faster rate it would have a higher station IATI cost regardless of subsequent volume but would use fewer train-hours. Most integral train terminals are so lightly utilized that their maintenance is nominal and independent of volume.

When it is proposed to use larger trains at an existing station, or to compromise station design when large trains are expected occasionally, planners must consider the effects of extending station time. The train's time value is several times the labor rate, so that extension will seldom reach a point where a second shift at the station is seriously considered.

Hence station time will usually be held to one shift or less. The terminal labor charge can usually include trip inspections of station gear while the train crewmen make the round trip from their base to the station — all in one shift.

It will usually develop that station charges are nearly a level figure *per trip*, regardless of volume.

### 3.6.2 Plant and Peripheral Costs

**Most industrial establishments, especially in the bulk trades, were designed around transportation limitations. An integral train system can usually allow some hitherto unavailable plant improvements. Plant managers, especially in the bulk-using trades, tend to the incorrect assumption that all change is to be resisted — they are an unscientific lot who fail to comprehend that the founders did what they could, not always what they wanted to do — hence "what is" is seldom best. An integral train planner should claim credit for the savings that his system will enable users to obtain.**

This illustration is taken from the blast furnace business. There are others. In a blast furnace plant an impressive array of conventional tools can be eliminated. Car thawing, car dumping, ore bridges, switchers, railroad yards, trestle men, and most mobile equipment can all be eliminated. These are important costs not ordinarily included in transportation budgets but made necessary by the transportation limitations that applied when each plant was designed.

An integral train system does not need as much space as most of the Lake-based systems. The space released can permit the next steel-making facility expansion (or modernization) to be made more economically. (Most steel mills have made improvements in which a new facility was put where there was room for it, not where it was wanted.) At this writing a new direct steel conversion process has just been announced — it should be at the cast house so the iron can flow directly into it from the blast furnace.

In most mills the ore yards represent the only opportunity for gaining strategically located space. However, most plant men will claim that this advantage has no value — "all the improvements have already been made." This family of intellectual barriers is part of the reason integral train studies are being made at this late date.

To cite a specific example, most Midwestern steel mills could put an integral train terminal on about half the space used by conventional systems.

In-plant switching is also important. The integral train will use one plant or railroad train crew for each delivery, regardless of size. The more congested the plant, the more the incentive to use a large train.

# 3.6.2

The planner must prepare for a series of irrational discussions. It is a fact that the integral train will pass through the plant — except where it can unload on the railroad outside the gate. (This, by the way, is most economic more often than might be expected, but it may require surrender of dual-line access and hence bargaining power.) It is true that it will, during its passage, "block" access to some parts of the mill. So did the switcher which no longer runs. More often, too.

Planners must be ready to reply to the claim: "But when this train comes in everything else must stop."

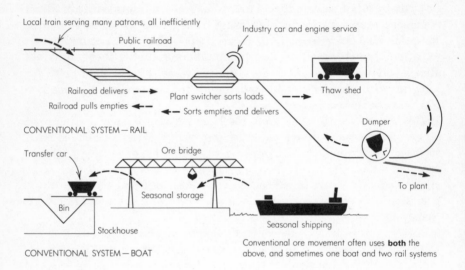

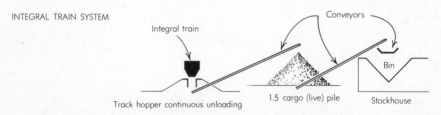

#### 3.6.2 — Blast Furnace Raw Material Delivery

The historic system involves repeated rehandling, in cars and in bulk, using costly equipment that demands considerable continuing maintenance. An integral train system permits continuous flow, using low-maintenance systems and few steps. "Shortening the process" produces considerable economy not otherwise available. When any process is shortened, steps taken out — and their cost — become further saving. Attempts to improve "efficiency" of what is there are inherently limited in potential, and the things that are done — e.g., new gadgets — involve new costs that consume part of the savings.

This is just not so. The fear is related to the fact that most trains stop and stand, and the reflex-action resistance to change — like Pavlov's dogs. The integral train does not stand — it moves and goes on its way.

*For example:* An ore-carrying integral train entering a plant may require 15 minutes to pass an important switch, during which time that switch is in use delivering iron ore. The same ore delivered in the usual manner will use that switch longer than 15 minutes. The train may be long enough to extend from the track hopper to a critical furnace entrance. It will occupy that crossing only after enough of the train has been unloaded to reach the crossing and then, at most, only long enough to pass the *rest* of the train over the hopper. Or it can be cut when needed — not necessarily every trip.

The only practical way to reply to this set of criticisms is:

First: Hear them all. Insist that each critic detail his problem and support whatever claim he makes about a "need" for continuous availability — and define "continuous availability" as *he* understands it.

Second: Prepare a detailed study, with times, etc., showing just what availability and occupancy presently exist at each allegedly critical location.

Third: Prepare a detailed study showing just what occupancy and availability would prevail with the most economic integral train operation. This condition will usually be more favorable than present conditions.

Fourth: Prepare a study showing what has to be done to obtain the conditions each critic *thinks* he now has — with costs in detail.

The next step will be obvious to all.

Integral train planners must depend on their knowledge, thoroughness, and ingenuity to observe and analyze. A car dumper, for example, usually has at least one locomotive and crew in attendance and incurs standby cost and yard cost. Transfer cars and ore bridges have heavy labor and maintenance cost — and sometimes scrap value and hence recoverable capital — as well as direct operating cost. Bulk car switching is usually combined, in plant accounts, with other traffic, and it requires some resourcefulness to estimate the differential effect that is defined as incremental saving. Caution is needed to avoid the usually unwarranted assumption that the plant railroad will still run as many engines as before if the bulk trade is moved to the integral train. The superintendent of the plant railroad may want it so, but the "organization man" treatment of always adding, never subtracting, is not the route to cost reduction. Parkinson's Law must be broken.

### 3.6.3 Inventory

The size of many integral trains suggests, incorrectly, a new need for inventory to accumulate a load. Actual inventory, in conventional rail-- roading, includes inventory in slow transit and inventory needed to protect against seasonal and irregular interruptions — and usually totals more than inventory in integral train systems. The emphasis on reliability in integral train system design thus becomes important in yet another way. When all pertinent variables — including those that traditionally are invisible and hence not counted — are studied, an integral train system usually can permit inventory reduction and consequent release of capital. The inventory will just be more visible.

All transportation involves more or less inventory. A distinction must be made between inventory carried to protect against interrup-

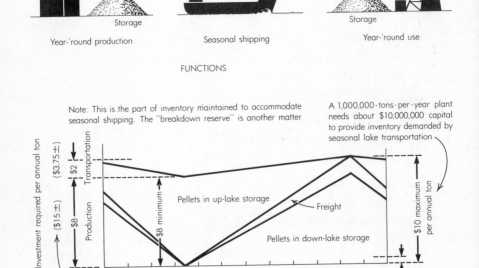

FUNCTIONS

3.6.3-A — Lake-Shipped Pellet Investments

The facts are concealed to most analysts because the steel industry has enough mental blocks and fragmented reporting to make concealment possible. An iron-ore pellet operation based on Great Lakes shipment involves a high fixed capital commitment — despite the fact that it is usually refinanced every year — and it is subject to inflation. The seasonal fluctuation in total capital commitment is limited to the transportation cost. Part of the concealment is made possible by the fact that the up-Lake and the down-Lake storage are usually carried in separate accounts.

tions in supply — a breakdown reserve — and that carried because the transportation system makes it necessary. Sometimes they are carried in one pile of material, and some people find it hard to make the distinction.

> *For example:* In the case of iron ore shipped on the Great Lakes the emergency reserve is that on hand when the first boat arrives in the spring — if one is to protect against an emergency one must assume it will happen at an inconvenient time. The rest of the inventory is needed to accommodate seasonal transportation and is a transportation cost whether it is in the rate or not.

In the case of Lakeborne iron ore pellets the pellet plant runs year-round, and there are two inventories whose total is about one half year's output. At a production cost of $15 to $16 per ton and a total transportation cost (plant to stockhouse) of $4 per ton, each annual ton of output involves inventory investment thus:

| | |
|---|---|
| Fall: Pellets | $7.50 - 8.00 |
| Transportation | $2.00 |
| Total | 9.50 - 10.00 at the steel mill |
| Spring: Pellets only | 7.50 - 8.00 at the up-Lake plant |

In the Lake trades an integral train system can be bought for less than this investment, including accessories. And the integral train investment is subject to I&A, thus generating cash flow. The inventory in pellets must be bought anew every year and so is subject to inflation.

> One shortsighted, pessimistic steel industry man objected to this reasoning with "But what if we stop using iron ore?" He owned the pellet plant.

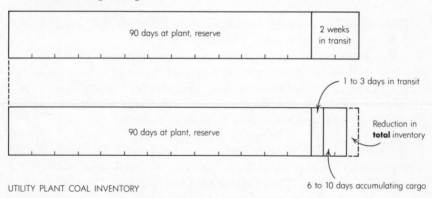

UTILITY PLANT COAL INVENTORY

### 3.6.3-B — Utility Plant Coal Reserve

Many profess to believe that the large sizes of economic integral trains will impose onerous storage demands on power plants. Such is not the case. The major storage demand is imposed by other requirements — usually the practice of holding a 90-day reserve to protect against unreliable labor — plus the space assigned to storing cars.

The integral train will reduce the transportation-forced part of the inventory to about two cargoes (two terminals and in-transit combined) or about 30¢ to 40¢ of inventory for each annual ton of movement — by running faster and more nearly continuously. Breakdown reserve must be added in both cases, but in the case of an integral train system it is (a) smaller and (b) most economically carried in an off-line location, such as a nearby empty lot, and not in vital in-plant space.

In the case of utility coal (except on Northern waterways) there need normally be no seasonal considerations. However, the average time in transit by conventional means is usually about the same as the time needed to accumulate a cargo and move it by integral train. Hence the inventory cost on this account is about an even offset. Most utility plants carry some 3 months' coal, and finding a place on the property for a few days' or even 2 or 3 weeks' inventory is no serious problem.

### 3.6.4 Loading and Unloading

In most integral train applications loading and unloading labor cost — including train crew from and to the nearest division point — will be a fixed cost per trip over most of the pertinent range. So will maintenance of conveyors and accessories — one inspection using 1 man-day or fraction per trip. Belt life will normally equal or exceed the amortization period of the system and hence belt replacement will seldom occur on account of volume. Most economically designed integral train terminals are lightly utilized to keep the costly train moving.

### 3.7 Budgeting

This section has used specific prices quite sparingly, for these reasons:
A — Any costs are subject to inflation.
B — Equipment development and improvements in related railroad practices can seriously affect costs — budgets in any industrial situation are valid only for a short time.
C — Conditions and requirements will vary widely among projects and each must be budgeted anew.
The second condition demands some comment:

*For example:* A study was made for a railroad client and proposed integral trains for a specific trade to be handled in a specific manner. The program was not followed through and its absence caused the traffic to move in other ways in response to what *was* made available. These other ways became established and were, themselves, significant in influencing patron site choices and equipment selections. Several years later an unimaginative railroad-employed planner sought to use the old scheme as it had been written and he found it inapplicable in the changed conditions. He was quite critical of studies that were not immune to changed environmental conditions and said, "But what if we *had* done what was proposed?"

Without allowing himself to "fill in an estimate form" — like a room-cooler salesman — an integral train planner is well advised to carry out his budgeting systematically. The following scheme will be found useful in most cases, provided it is used intelligently and not mechanically.

Budget incremental costs first. "Markups" and allocations of fixed costs differ in *kind* and must be reviewed separately. Arrange costs to be budgeted in major groups. These are suggested:

System costs — which sometimes must later be allocated to
    traffic components to satisfy management requirements.
Time costs of the trains themselves.
Mileage-based costs that can then be combined for deriving
    subtotals for individual trips.
Miscellaneous railroad event or trip costs.
Time costs of the terminals.
Event or trip costs for the terminals.
Work-load costs such as fuel, etc.
All other incremental costs.

Costs are most conveniently derived, first, in terms of units for the trains to be used in any specific case — such a practice avoids a great deal of computation which must be carried out and then checked.

*For example:* Once the train size has been selected, determine its total hourly cost and its total cost per mile, also its combined fuel and engine supply cost per hour at various loads.

System costs can be most easily estimated if the following items are accounted for:

Management and supervision
Sales, if applicable
Royalties, rents and the like
Insurance, whether bought or self-insured
Review for specials, if any.

Time costs of the trains will usually include:

IATI (use cost, not rent quotations)
Periodic maintenance
Protective services — e.g., storage, idling when not in ser-
    vice, etc.
Review for specials, if any.

Mileage costs will usually include:

Wheels, axles and bearings
Road crew costs
Track maintenance
Review for specials, if any.

Railroad trip and event costs will usually include:
Formal inspections
Functional inspections and repair allowances
Supervisors, towermen, switch tenders, crew arbitraries and
extras
Crew trip expenses — e.g., taxis, lodgings
Wheelage charges, pilots, consequential delays if applicable,
tolls
Review for specials, if any.
Terminal time costs usually include:
IATI for terminal facilities, usually reported separately and al-
located to traffic components only if necessary
Major maintenance in rare cases
Review for specials, if any.
Terminal trip or event costs usually include:
Terminal labor
Supervision, in some cases
Railroad or plant facility train delivery crews
Review for specials, if any.
Work load costs usually include:
Fuel and supplies (usually a percentage of fuel)
Some elements of equipment maintenance and shop costs
Terminal power and maintenance material
Review for specials, if any.

These costs are usually most useful if they are derived in the form of a table of units adapted to the particular operation and then combined (all but the annual system costs and terminal time costs) into costs per round trip or otherwise defined mission.

This "cost per mission" can then be used to report the incremental cost of performing a mission — e.g., as running a train one round trip over the route, including loading and unloading it. It will also usually be informative to separate this total into three subdivisions:

Work that must be done and hence costs that must be incurred
by the railroad — e.g., train crews.
Work that must be done by and hence costs that must be incurred by patrons — e.g., terminal labor.
Work that can be done by and hence costs that can be incurred
by the railroad *or* patron — e.g., train ownership.

Some managements will also want cash flow data. In such cases it is useful to extract:

All I&A (classified appropriately, including credit for impending capital outlays the system can forestall.
All savings of actual present or otherwise needed expenses
— e.g., transfer car operators to be phased out — and anticipated increases thereof.
All eliminated direct costs for other services.

Freight rates will usually not enter into discussions at this stage so that *rate* "savings" are only of marginal interest. Many managements will want to see them, though. In such cases make a separate calculation comparing integral train system incremental costs with rate-plus-peripheral-costs and *interpret* the comparison.

Capital outlays must usually be reported in some detail. It is advisable to report all capital items, classified in three groups:

Those which must be made by the railroad (usually none).

Those which must be made by patrons (usually a few).

Those which may be made by railroad, patron, leasing company or other — e.g., buy the train (usually most of the project).

Capital offsets — e.g., scrapped existing tools, liquidated inventory and forestalled impending costs — should normally be reported in each group and in total. IATI computations should *not* take offsets into account, but their effect should be shown in an economic summary.

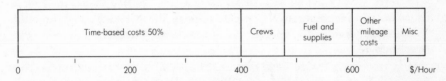

**3.7 — Major Integral Train Cost Elements**

This diagram illustrates a typical distribution of costs among major elements for a wide range of integral train situations, though each operation must be studied separately. For example, if a train is run slowly, the time costs will greatly increase because the saving in power ratio cannot be enough to buy the additional cars, fuel, and other costs. Crew costs will decline in terms of time units but *not* in terms of trip units if trips are prolonged. Fuel and supplies on a trip basis will increase with slow operation. This scale is applicable to a train of medium size. The proportions are generally applicable to many systems.

# 4. COMMERCIAL EXPLOITATION

Commercial exploitation will use cost figures, together with the art — not science — of motivating people. The basic rationale is that the potential profit must be divided among all those whose cooperation is needed, and each needs incentive. The process of dividing the profits is called rate-making and must not be confused with conventional rates and divisions, which usually deal with gross, not with net. Conventional operations do not permit identifying profit as integral train systems do. The rationale encounters "practical" limitations — and other means are then needed — when it is found that policy men and decision makers in many industries, including transportation, are not always moved to action merely by the prospect of profit for their companies. And it does not follow the shippers' gain is carriers' loss or vice versa. Many people still think all changes are just "blackmailing a railroad." In fact, nearly all projects offer to share savings and the only "blackmail" involved is on the conceptual level, directed to people who fear change.

It is necessary to review certain phases of cost estimating in the framework of commercial exploitation. Distinctions among "costs" computed for various purposes must be understood. Shipper, carrier and common interests must be understood, as must the impact of cost differentials in areas traditionally isolated from transport rate discussions. And — not least — commercial considerations include some that cannot be analyzed.

A shipper, seeking low rates, must assure that cost data does not overstate costs or include as "variable" anything that should be part of fixed costs. He must also assure that cost studies properly show how inexpensive other means *can* be as well as how inexpensively integral trains *can* be run.

Shippers will encourage railroad men to overstate conventional system costs (few need much encouragement, and conventional system costs *are* high). A railroad man then faces a dilemma — admit to high profits in conventional railroading, accept integral train profits smaller than he had but larger than he admitted, or look irrational to shippers, regulators and stockholders.

Obviously one railroad use of such studies is to force clear thinking about costs — to avoid such dilemmas. Sooner or later someone will force a legal test on the premise that failure to avail oneself of such technological opportunity imposes a burden on interstate commerce — and on all shippers — thus defining a positive duty to progress on the part of regulated (protected) carriers.

One problem of commercial exploitation is to avoid distortions. To do so, cost studies must extend in scope to all pertinent matters and permit comparing totals — all dollars are equally important. Traditional costs and rates are independent of each other — except where they are the tools of what amounts to market-rigging. A planner meeting a flat demand that a rate be maintained to "protect" a shipper needs ingenuity — cost reduction per se is what is under attack.

One use of an integral train system in this seemingly hopeless situation is to devise a service that is as novel as possible to justify a break with traditional pricing rationale, remove as much of the rate equivalent from regulation and public view as possible and so frustrate comparison — quite the reverse of the usual effort to make the new resemble the old as much as possible.

Various special rates will be needed — e.g., "dump" or "space available" rates can exploit train time bought with time-bonus money. Incentives to promptness must be without arbitrary end — e.g., no "free" time because "free time" really is time charged for whether used or not.

Financing is simplified when the nature of time costs is understood — capital is bought like any other commodity from whatever vendor most wants the account. But sooner or later someone wants to know who guarantees the profits.

> *For example:* An iron miner wants a blast furnace operator
> to guarantee to buy his pellets. But no one guarantees to buy
> the steel. Such a "miner" is a money lender and labor contrac-
> tor and gets the wages of money lenders and labor contractors.
> The steel company-entrepreneur expects the entrepreneurial
> profit.

Many lengthy financing discussions can be shortened when all concerned are asked whether they want to be money lenders or entrepreneurs. If there is no entrepreneur there is no deal. If someone — e.g., a chemical company — is already an entrepreneur to the extent of a chemical plant, he can reasonably put equity money into an integral train system, accessory to his chemical plant, for a rate of return as good as he could get elsewhere — e.g., in his chemical plant — and borrow the rest from someone who wants to be a money lender. But he cannot have it both ways. There are two "profits." One is wages or interest for the money lender — which is not really profit in this context — and the other is residual or entrepreneurial profit.

Most regulatory problems are best handled by isolating as much of the operation as possible. The reasons are similar to those which lead to isolating as much of the operation as possible from railroad management. The condition also helps a railroader to accept the plan, because it insulates him from the "buy me one, too" shippers who cannot profitably use such systems. An aggressive railroad salesman will not wait to be approached; he will be out selling.

## 4.1 Traditional and Conventional Costing

Most conventional costing systems are based on accounting practices and serve *their* purposes more or less adequately. Cost estimating for planning purposes differs from these traditional schemes because the objectives differ. The distinction between estimates and forecasts on the one hand and accounts on the other must be understood. The accountant is a historian. The designer is a forecaster.

As earlier noted, integral train planning and design estimates will use the construction estimator's methods. Planners' estimates are not necessarily ideal or appropriate for pricing or selection of commercial strategy. Neither are traditional costing systems.

This review of traditional costing elements in the context of integral train planning is not a costing textbook. It is a set of warnings to help avoid serious obstacles. Most integral train planners will encounter costing problems, largely in coping with unfounded objections to their proposals — even after doing the cost work needed to develop a sound design. The planner must understand the limitations of his critics' basic premises. All his work *at this point* is in a commercial context where prices are "what the traffic will bear" and "estimates" are made to win conferences — by now his design should have been made and he should have his supporting data at hand.

### 4.1.1 Orthodox Transportation Costing

Most transportation cost "systems" — e.g., ICC accounting systems — reflect the presence of large fixed costs and, primarily, they comprise essentially arbitrary bases for allocating common costs. Most of them have been in use for so long that the present generation of managers think they are real — or immutable. Men now active found them already in use; hence they fall into the inheritors' characteristic disabilities. The law demands keeping such a set of books, and managers understandably seem to believe that if they have — at great cost — prepared a set of numbers, they must be useful for something besides satisfying government inspectors. This condition inhibits choices based on the effect of variables that *can* be controlled or at least influenced.

An integral train planner must complete his cost forecasts, undertaking to forecast or estimate incremental costs in detail before entering into any discussion of costs computed in any other way. By definition the incremental cost computation details those costs that will be incurred if an integral train runs and which will not be incurred if it does not run. Therefore it must be used as *half* of the basis for discussing the probable effects on the balance sheet — with which all businesses have a concern. (The other half is the rate level, which is a function of the market and independent of costs.)

It will be informative, after the detailed incremental cost computation is done and "rate" discussions are under way, to compare this estimate with the "cost" forecast that the railroads involved will usually prepare — and use as "evidence" of their need for high rates. An item-by-item comparison is helpful if the principals cannot otherwise reach agreement on division of profits.

A traditional or conventional cost study will usually devote much of its effort to establishing the amounts that the proposed operation "should" contribute to fixed costs (though they may be seldom so defined — the planner must reason, not read labels, and must reject "catch-all" groupings). In the commercial sense, the contribution to fixed costs is all the traffic will bear despite the fact that cost estimators may differ on just what is the actual outlay and what is allocated or imputed. When a sophisticated railroader wants to divorce cost from rate discussions, a shipper's gambit is to demand conventional service

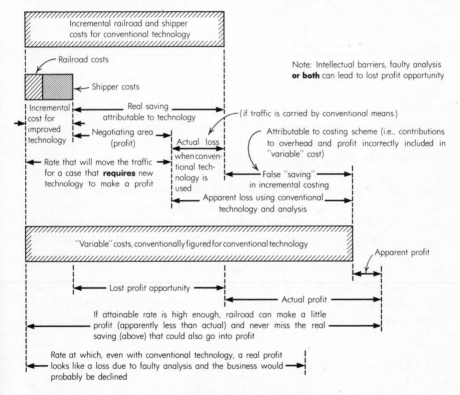

#### 4.1.1 — Real and Apparent Savings

It will be obvious that actual savings may differ from "savings" computed by any arbitrary formula. It is also obvious that the rate equivalent must reflect a division of potential savings or profits. The total of railroad and shipper costs is the pertinent planning basis in a rational system, regardless of the formal or legal definition of "rates."

and numerous "priveleges." By then a sophisticated railroader will be willing to discuss cost differentials with a view to dividing them.

The problem of allocation will arise in two ways. One is direct allocation. The other is the use of some variations of "average" or "system" costs whereby certain costs that are themselves variable, but do not vary with the alternatives under discussion, are included as "direct" costs.

Planners are thus cautioned that what the conventional transportation cost systems call "variable" do not all vary with the alternates under consideration.

Another variation of cost disagreement that will arise is the claim that any traffic available — some go so far as to be indifferent to whether it is on the rails or not — is deemed to be obliged to share in the costs of unremunerative functions such as branch lines and local trains. It is often claimed, or at least implied, in costing systems that if any element of traffic demands such services, all should be required to use them to justify allocating their costs more widely. Those who reason so usually also claim new traffic should be rejected if its contribution to such external (to it) costs is less than they consider "equitable." Such an attitude is tantamount to indifference to the profit and loss position, and the planner cannot be reticent in illuminating the fallacy.

A further element of controversy will be stated essentially this way:
But our present costing systems reflect the long-term costs that we incur. Nothing that changes the economics of one part of the traffic can greatly affect this condition.

The reply is:
An integral train system, properly applied, can produce long-term improvements in the economics of railroading. If your costing system denies the profits of the improvements to those who create them, there never will be a start toward improvement, and large shippers will increasingly be forced to private road, water, pipeline or wire line carriage.

At its most cynical, attempts to use traditional costing systems are equivalent to attempts to increase the amount of money that the railroad expects to be paid *before* undertaking division of the net savings the improvements can bring about.

### 4.1.2 Industrial Costing Systems

**Most industrial costing systems reflect the need to allocate common costs. But they also reflect inventory and its value variations — an important item in manufacturing and trading operations. Most of them seek to determine a unit cost to simplify managerial thought processes.**

In simple cases it works well enough. When choices among alternatives are complex — as in engineering design and in pricing transportation — this process usually leads to anomalies. Most conflicts with industrial cost men will be in the area of burden rates whether so labeled or not. In incremental costing there simply are no such things as burden rates as usually understood (though the phrase is unfortunately often used with a special meaning).

In discussions with industrial cost men it is usually helpful to point out that an incremental cost computation is *arithmetically* comparable to a "dumping" computation and that it is used as a tool for decision making, not as a rate base.

When working for shippers, the incremental cost computation usually is most easily made clear if components are reported separately for the work done by the railroad (which should be held to a minimum) and for work done by the shipper and/or his contractor (which should be maximized). Then the resulting budget can be presented to shippers thus:

> The budgeted total transportation cost will be incurred by you and the railroad. This report tells just what money the railroad *has* to spend. You will pay them more than that to give them a profit and pay for the use of their sunk-cost plant and their monopoly of routes. You will pay the rest of the cost yourself, directly or through contractors, some of whom may be railroads — but that is unlikely. The tabulation includes capital recovery and return on your investments, but you need not pay anyone a markup on it if you keep it in the house.

This approach usually gets across at the executive level — the problem is one of communications, not technique.

### 4.1.3 "Standard" Costs

Some personality types are comforted by anything called "standard." In many applications "standard" costs substitute for analytical thought. In some cases the "system" generates supposedly objective variances — usually from accounting data and always historical, and usually printed in red to motivate people to remove them. They are nearly always essentially arbitrary numbers, however derived, and the perceptive people they should motivate — the very people who *could* create improvements — direct their talents to decoding the system and beating it.

Such "standard" costs will seldom be introduced into integral train system planning if the planner has — early and adequately — informed those involved about the nature of the task in hand.

It is inherent in the philosophy of "standard" costs that a technique or system for carrying out a function is established — "mature" — and that what is being measured is the effectiveness of lower-level managers in using *that* established system. It is inherent in the philosophy of integral train systems *at the present state of the art* that what is under discussion is a new way of using the tools — not standard by definition.

If a planner finds himself beset by a "standard" cost rationale, he can take this condition as evidence that he did not do the original indoctrination adequately. There is nothing for it but to become a teacher again.

### 4.1.4  Nonapplicability of Orthodox Cost Systems

**Traditional cost systems are of little use in the design or exploitation of integral train systems, except to understand the mental processes of the people who must be motivated. They must be comprehended so that planners can anticipate some of the problems.**

It should be evident at this point that an integral train planner who finds himself in conflict with proponents of standard, conventional or traditional cost systems needs to do some education. When this condition arises he must do some homework with whichever of the popular texts his antagonist used.

Conventional or orthodox systems nearly always lead — in transportation situations — to supporting a "no changes" position because they are nearly all designed to penalize departures from the past. It can safely be assumed that any integral train planner is not using the traditional systems himself but has adopted the construction estimator's methods — because those "philosophies" were designed precisely to measure the value of departures from past technology.

It should also be clear at this point that costing systems are not directly involved in the pricing process.

### 4.2  Pricing

**Pricing anything is essentially a commercial task. And it makes a difference whether a planner is buying or selling. Theoretically a price is as high as it can be and still get the trade, or as low as a vendor thinks he has to go. This process calls for evaluating alternatives — which looks simple, and every traffic man thinks he knows how. However, one alternative is an integral train on some other line, and it has commercial properties that are new to most transportation men. To cite just one — an integral train system contains, in an intellectually and conceptually inseparable package, some functions located in shipper and in receiver plants. Total package costs must be compared**

with the sum of costs of corresponding elements, wherever found, in alternative schemes. Few transportation men are accustomed to "invading" the patron's cost structure — much less operating regime — for such analysis. And it won't help just to "ask the man," either.

When a shipper hires the planner this condition can be exploited by introducing this rationale:

> Savings in shipping and receiving plants belong to the shipper and receiver. All needed investments are chargeable to the system. Now let us reason together and negotiate a division of the savings which the integral train system will enable the railroad to make when we, the shipper, allow the changes its use requires.

Few railroad men will see the anomaly. It is too much like the traditional arrangements.

A variant is to propose integral train rates directly competitive with other rates, with due allowance for real or supposed rail and integral train disability — consisting of in-plant costs without commenting on in-plant savings. Many railroaders are easily convinced of the inevitable disabilities of integral trains — they represent changes. This writer's experience includes several cases in which rail traffic men voluntarily charged themselves disabilities for things that actually would justify premiums. "Different," therefore "inferior," has many adherents.

Also to a shipper's advantage in negotiations, integral train technology has the property of permitting precise and reliable cost estimating. The rate "discussion" goes like this:

> "The rate you have been charging me is exorbitant — I have to carry more than my share of fixed costs." The conditioned-reflex usually is a poor-mouth reply. The railroader replies that he is barely breaking even. His testimony at the last rate hearing was to that effect. Sometimes he is — his technology is incredibly primitive. A shipper then proposes an integral train and a cost-based rate which contributes to fixed costs at a known level, higher than the railroader admits — or sometimes even knows — is in the conventional rate and service.

An integral train system has the capability of developing lower costs on the road *and* in the patron's plant. For a railroad to exploit this capability demands estimating *all* of these savings. If it sounds like telling the patron how to run his business, so be it. The process is used by most vendors to help patrons use their products or services most effectively. But the planner must know or learn a great deal about his patron's business and how it runs — and how it *could* run — how the founding fathers would have built it if they could. "Inheritor" managements in industry are just as reluctant as in railroading to try to improve on the compromises that were forced on the founders by conditions that *then* existed.

Changes in patron operating practices frighten the timid traffic men — they will be reluctant to "dictate" changes. Most of the changes, though, are changes patron plant men would have made long ago if transportation limitations would permit. The integral train seldom forces change — if often permits change, even if negotiators for one side or the other call the changes concessions.

*For example:* One man with well-fixed ideas said, "You offer compelling economic incentives that I cannot pass by and so you are forcing me to do something. I don't like to be forced and I wont do it." He didn't. His competitor did. He's not there anymore.

A clear understanding of costs and competition — and a sound business rationale — will help to deal with the arbitraries like artificial rate differentials, traffic allocation practices and the like — including blind resistance to change wherever found.

### 4.2.1  Pricing Concepts and Rationale

In any business, total revenue from any element must first pay all of its incremental costs, and only then can it contribute to overhead and profit. The concept applies first to entire operations or functions. The scope of a comparison must be large enough to encompass all alternatives, and hence the concept may not be applicable to parts that are arbitrarily defined.

The division of the task, and hence of investments and revenues, is a matter of policy, not related to engineering. Obviously each party in a joint venture — formal or informal — must get a division adequate to cover the incremental costs of that part of the task assigned him — and as much of the part of gross left over after all incremental costs as he can get at the conference table.

The total value of a transportation service is usually difficult to determine. However, in a conversion project it can be approached this way (example from iron ore, applicable everywhere with suitable adaptations):

| | |
|---|---|
| Present or attainable freight rate (if client is a shipper; otherwise use costs) | XXX |
| Dock charges and other intermediates | XX |
| In-plant switching, car thawing, dumping, car cleaning, etc. | XXX |
| Ore bridge, transfer car, inventory | XX |
| Ownership, operation and maintenance of plant used | XX |
| Present total price | XXX $=$ Pt (by definition) |

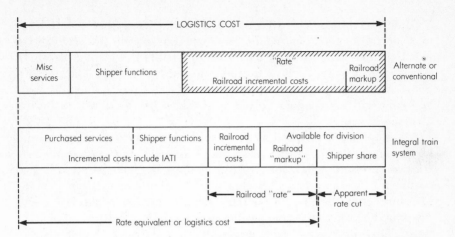

Note: "Rate" is usually something regulated carriers charge for
whatever they do. Fuzzy and varying definitions often inhibit
informative comparisons

Realistically, "railroad markup" should increase to elicit railroad cooperation

### 4.2.1 — Cost Elements

Total cost is the economic criterion. When interest and amortization are listed among
costs, regardless of whose capital is used, there is no question of investment to obtain
a saving. When the question is asked in the form "How much do I have to invest to get
this saving?" then the reply should include, in "saving," the interest and amortization
as well as what is rationally called net saving, or should be "Nothing. I have included
the cost of someone else's money in the costs." This is not entirely adequate as a reply
but it will usually serve to get the discussion moving in a useful direction. In the example, the railroad "rate" would include railroad cost plus the railroad markup, but the
rate equivalent should include all the things carrier and shipper combined must do and
should be compared with corresponding totals for other systems. Planners are cautioned
to insist on rational treatment when shippers expect "standby" or intermittent service
wihout appearing to pay for it, or want a railroad to make a speculative investment
and conceal the speculator's profit.

An integral train incremental cost computation will yield a number
in three parts:
$$Ci = Cir + Cip + Cix$$
where: $Ci$ = incremental cost
$Cir$ = incremental costs necessarily incurred
by railroads
$Cip$ = incremental costs necessarily incurred
by patrons
$Cix$ = incremental costs for which there is a
choice as to allocation

"Profit" can be defined as:
$$P = Pt - Ci$$
and must be adjusted to account for the parts of Pt that will continue
if the operation is replaced.

Some of this profit can be assigned to the work that the railroad must perform and commercially must equal or exceed the profit in the existing rates. The railroad will try to overstate this item if it can, of course, but it cannot afford to make present rates seem extortionate. Some can be allocated to the part of the work the patron must perform, and some will be "vendors'" profit on purchased services where there is a choice of sources.

A variation occurs when some other proposed system offers savings when compared to present practices. Rationally the procedure is to treat as "present" whatever alternative offers the next best set of total economics. It is assumed, of course, that the parties are seriously trying to bring about the most economic systems and are concerned about dividing the profit, lest some profit escape for lack of agreement on divisions. This reservation rules out conflict-of-interest and unsupported intellectual rigidity situations.

> *For example:* If a railroad has an incremental cost below the best a barge can do, it is letting money get away (and so is the shipper) if it does not get the trade, going slightly under the (equivalent) barge rate if necessary to do so. In such a case a shipper who "just does not like railroads" is spending the stockholders' money to cater to his prejudice — which is a private affair as long as he is honest about it.

### 4.2.2 Competition

There is always another way. Each "way to do the job" has a cost — for certain. The proprietor of the lowest-cost "way" can theoretically set his price just under the next lowest and get the order. Most suboptimal efforts to evaluate competition omit some alternatives and components. This is particularly true in integral train system planning because such systems can generate savings in adjacent areas traditionally not included in transportation — and few transportation men study matters beyond their traditional areas of concern.

Whether the integral train planner is working for railroad or shipper, he should study the potentials of all competitors — all feasible railroad routes as well as other modes of transport and some nontransportation choices such as decentralization — this last is called re-sourcing, a particularly unfortunate choice of name.

As noted elsewhere, in an open economy the comparison each main and subsystem choice must survive is with the next in the heirarchy of descending economy. In the case of railroad routes, the trend to mergers is fast removing opportunities for competition in North America. Fortunately or unfortunately, the integral train system is usually more economic than any other available scheme (where it is applicable at all) and, with mergers, monopoly in transportation may soon be restored. Holding rates up, at shippers' expense, to preserve "competition" seems self-defeating.

For these reasons real competition will not always be found, but the matter must be studied in each case to bring the costs down to practical levels and so gain some of the benefits of the new technology.

### 4.2.3 "Rate Structures"

Most common-carrier rates contain long-established relationships that exist by fiat or are considered inviolate. Most exist to "protect" some market allocation.

For example: One railroad that tried to pass on some savings in ex-Lake iron ore haulage found itself in court. It was claimed that the "natural advantages" of Lakefront furnaces had to be preserved by artificially maintained inland rates that disadvantaged interior furnaces.

Others are the mechanism of a cartel — even when the goods do not actually move by common carrier.

For example: The Kansas wheat price is "freight off the Gulf," though actual movement is largely nonregulated. A proposed lower common-carrier rate, to get it some business, was resisted because this would raise the Kansas price and disadvantage a Kansas flour mill that did not use transportation, thus disturbing a market allocation.

For example: Many industries still use variations of "basing point" prices in which common-carrier published rates from arbitrary points are used to fix retail prices, regardless of actual movements or manufacturing locations.

Such arrangements have been attacked in various ways, with varying degrees of success under antimonopoly laws or philosophies. Still, they persist.

This condition is one of the facts of commercial life and it is also a fact of commercial life that few dare to admit such motivations in public. Some of the resistance to the new technology is based on self-preservation — of those who exist behind the shelter of freight rate barriers. Some such are private businesses and some are public agencies. The integral train planner's response will depend on whether he is working for a shipper or a railroad.

If he is working for a shipper he will seek to have as much of the program as possible taken out of railroad hands to frustrate attempts to make direct comparisons. At the same time he will use this minimum railroad participation to pressure it into accepting minimum contributions to overhead and profit — its "markup" will look extortionate when it is referred to a very low participation, whether it is actually equitable or not.

In this situation a railroad man can reflect that this is what happens when he tries to or helps to operate a cartel that would probably be, at least, questionable if operated openly. And one that seldom helps him, at that.

If the integral train planner is working for a railroad he will usually insist on keeping as much of the operation as possible himself — e.g., supply the train at least (or in a wholly owned subsidiary to isolate it from connections) — and use it to widen his profit margin on the present rates. To do so he must usually provide all the accessories himself, including terminals, regardless of traditional divisions. He then must defend himself against pressures to supply trains to those who cannot effectively use them. Such defense is best made by offering time-charters, by the hour and not by the week or month.

There does not seem to be any way to have it both ways. Planners will save considerable time and energy by going directly to the central issue and avoiding lengthy arguments on peripheral camouflage issues.

### 4.2.4 Traffic Allocation

**Traditional rates, often set under monopoly conditions, were fixed by little more than tests of political strength — a business was "entitled to" or "needed" a rate that enabled it to survive such misfortunes as poor choice of plant sites — and no one knew what transportation service cost anyway. "Competitive" rates were equal and traffic men allocated traffic among competitors according to the solicitors' skills or the sizes of their expense accounts. In sophisticated competition, based on economic capability, such allocation is not feasible. Rates high enough to permit such practices — by concealing their costs — are wasteful, and when integral trains are used the waste is visible — and may be embarrassing.**

To the extent that mergers are removing route choices, the practice of wasteful allocation to circuitous routes is declining in importance. To the extent that such routes remain, disadvantaged roads will continue to press for rates high enough to enable them to make a profit — when they know what their costs are — on whatever "fair share" of the traffic they can get.

Proprietors of inherently or potentially low-cost routes will help competitors take their traffic from them to the extent that they hold effective rates high enough to protect such practices. When the shipper provides most of the equipment and facilities, he is not likely to use the less economic route, since he is paying the extra costs involved — and knows that they are.

If a shipper intends to practice traffic allocation he will do so, and an integral train planner can do little about it — antieconomic choices are often beyond rational treatment. Sometimes a railroad will be reluctant to offer a conclusively economic integral train system for, say, iron ore, lest the steel company deny it the finished-goods traffic — to preserve the traffic man's rapport with all railroad solicitors. In such a case, the fact is that the steel company's customers control the finished-goods routing and such threats are largely empty. Emotional conduct in this area does exist, but this writer finds its incidence overstated in most quarters.

In this family of problems it appears that a strictly and basically honest policy of competition at all levels — economic and intellectual — is the one most likely to produce *long-term* benefits.

### 4.2.5 "Dump" Rates

**The need for reliability demands reserve capacity. Cost control requires that railroads be paid a bonus for train time, thus making surplus capacity available. Efficiency demands that this capacity be sold when it is available — when the delay allowed for does not occur or when a railroad consistently brings the train back early. Such service can be offered on a space-available basis.**

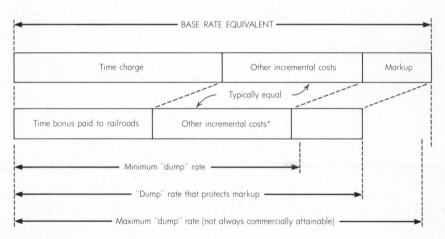

*Adjust for use of "base-case" facilities as appropriate — usually reduced below corresponding component in base rate

**4.2.5 — "Dump" Rates**

The time bonus will be less than the original time charge, but *most* other incremental costs for trips made with this time will be the same as for any other trips. Any attainable rate higher than the sum of time-bonus and nontime incremental costs will add to profit, but rates should be "all the traffic will bear."

In the bulk trades such capacity is produced in terms of train time. A dispatcher must usually manage the trains in his fleet like a taxicab dispatcher so that train time is available where it can be used.

The "space available" business will usually be in some commodity like coal or off-season potash moved from one or more mines to a "warehouse" at a "port" for movement by barge, car or truck to varied customers — usually customers who could not be readily served directly by integral train. The rate to be charged for such service will, like all other rates, be what the traffic will bear. The cost of such service will be less than it otherwise would be. This is true because the time cost of the train is the amount of the time bonus, which should be less than the time cost of the train in its original application. It will usually develop that the "space available" movement will be from producers who also ship on the base rate so that duplication of loading facilities does not result. It follows that a further reduction in unit cost will occur because the ownership or time cost of loading facilities is not incurred on the additional volume.

A "space available" condition in a container train operation will arise just like it does on an airline. Such services will usually be rigidly and symmetrically scheduled, and when the train is about to leave there may be vacant slots. In such cases the "space available" or "standby" shippers should have their containers on hand for last-minute loading. Again, the rate is whatever the traffic will bear — in some cases on a sliding scale declining with delay.

### 4.2.6 "Costs" for Various Uses

**There is no "true cost." It should be clear that "cost" calculations made for decision-making, accounting and pricing purposes will vary from each other, if for no other reason than that each ordinarily omits items not related to the purpose at hand.**

*For example:* Costs calculated for decision-making omit all elements that are fixed — i.e., do not vary — with respect to the variable about which a decision is needed.

*For example:* Accounting costs measure, in effect, success or failure in meeting earlier forecasts, and so measure the accuracy of the forecasts as well.

*For example:* Cost computations for use in pricing seek to establish what cost alternatives exist and that any proposed price will or will not contribute to those costs that exist whether the business is handled or not.

## 4.3 Financing

Financing is a cloudy matter. The first reaction to an integral train proposal is usually one of fear of the supposedly large sums of capital required. This conditioned reflex, applied to most proposals for change, is aggravated by the fact that much facility planning is done by equipment vendors uninterested in minimizing capital — they seek to maximize sales.

Industrial progress has moved toward capital intensity, and integral train technology has one serious acceptability weakness in this respect. It is quite often less costly to use more labor than more capital — e.g., hire a yard crew for a whole day instead of buying more equipment to use a slower schedule — and such a condition makes many managers vaguely uneasy, even aside from the general desire to minimize labor per se. Integral train technology offers no way to conceal such facts. It also elicits complaints from labor-oriented critics because its labor content is lower than historic, superficially similar, transportation systems.

Financing must be a purely commercial matter. Capital is available, at some price, in any quantity. Given this premise, it is immediately apparent that return on capital is not profit. Return on capital — i.e., rental on money like rental on anything else — is a cost, to be included with other costs before counting profit, no matter who supplies the capital.

There usually are alternatives. The object is to minimize *total* cost, including capital costs. A dollar invested in patron fixed plant is just as important as a dollar in inventory or train; a dollar for capital service is just as important as a dollar in wages. Narrow scope in an engineering economy study conceals these relationships by excluding some kinds of alternates and usually does not affect all alternates uniformly.

Planners should examine *all* pertinent capital requirements. For example, much or all of an integral train system can sometimes be bought with capital released from other commitments ("salvage") which the integral train can make unnecessary. *Net* capital is what must be charged to the *decision* to change — and it can be negative. Incidentally, salvage arises either from liquidation of existing tangibles or from outlays forstalled.

> *For example:* A new mineral processing plant needs a loading facility. An integral train system can usually use a less costly facility than any other available system. The difference is a capital credit — negative capital — in the decision-making process. Until the plant is built.

All capital should be budgeted for interest and recovery — including "roll-over" inventory capital. (The practice of so budgeting is not usual and such capital is thus concealed.) All assets should be assigned short lives in view of possible early obsolescence. Tax policies that forbid reporting recovery at suitable rates are irrelevant to the planning process — that adjustment comes later. Cash-flow rationale usually favors integral train systems, partly because they can reduce inventory or substitute amortizable, inflation-proof investments for inventory.

*For example:* A Great Lakes taconite plant operating on Lake carriage requires seasonal investment about equal to one third of the plant investment. It is usually "roll-over" capital switched back and forth from one account to another annually to make it look liquid. But it is not amortized and it must be produced from somewhere every year — it can be recovered only by closing the operation, and it increases with inflation. An integral train system for this application can be bought for about the same investment, not subject to inflation and written off year by year to generate cash flow.

Leases, like internally generated capital, and the like are only alternate forms of borrowing — all must be amortized and equity returns must be computed *after* financing costs. These basic principles are elementary to any student of capital application — but integral train planners will need to reiterate them.

### 4.3.1 Rental of Money

Sec. 3.1.1 defined IATI. In commercial exploitation part of this money is in "cash flow" if the capital is internally generated. This element is important when the integral train is used as a substitute for some other kinds of investment or when leasing vs. buying is under consideration.

There have been instances in which large sums of money have been spent on mistaken beliefs in this area. One example will illustrate:

An industrial management decided to use a unit train system for coal in which it would supply cars and the railroad would supply power. The railroad insisted on immediate return of empties from the power plant. The consultant made two errors:

A — He included only one choice in his plant alternatives — one involving high investment — and excluded schemes that needed design work — possibly because his fee did not permit original design.

B — He assumed (unrealistically) that cars could be owned on a contingent basis whereby their cost could be escaped if his client elected to go to nuclear power, and that plant investment could not be so financed.

Actually there are many variations of plant lease-back arrangements, and this company had been using them for some kinds of assets but not for others. This industry concluded that $1 in plant investment was equivalent to $4 in cars because it chose to limit and define financing alternatives differently for the two kinds of investment. Then it eliminated design choices for plant improvements to those that did not require original engineering and so excluded those that would have survived even this harsh criterion. To this writer's knowledge the banks involved regarded the cars in exactly the same way as this customer's plant assets.

This example is but one of many, and it illustrates an important point. Vendors of money are in a competitive market, too, but one in which little is spent on sales. The sales effort is found in the equipment business. Equipment salesmen spend considerable of their time and energy in planning ways to sell money (at a profit) along with the hardware — the "trade-up" and the "tie-in." A system planner who allows *any* salesman to do some of his planning for him must expect the planning to serve the interests of him who does it.

In the illustration, a car salesman put together the package and made a sale. The user committed himself to pay at least $2,000,000 more than he otherwise would have paid out. The fixed-plant salesman concluded that if he had to settle for a small sale (a low-capital alternate), or if he had to sell money, too, he was not interested. The user got what he sought — low-budget engineering. And a little bit of a snow job to the effect that if basic fuel economics changed so drastically that he would scrap his existing coal-burning power plants, there would be someone to buy his secondhand cars.

### 4.3.2 Reserve and Standby Provisions

Reserve equipment is provided by including delay time allowances in schedules. It is usually more informative and less likely to error to provide such allowances in detail for each element or function than to try to choose an overall "spare ratio." The common practice of assigning reserve and standby equipment as a system cost tends to obscure differences among routes, equipment and methods, especially when the differences are in reliability. Alternatives often include more inventory, standby services by other means — e.g., common carriers — etc. Adequate direct standby in each schedule is more visible but is usually recommended — despite the fact that it elicits defensive reactions that must simply be endured. There is no need to plan separate financing for spares as "system overhead" when they are correctly

**budgeted in each function. This condition is a manifestation of the basic policy of exhibiting traditionally hidden costs, for rational reasons.**

This practice sometimes leads to error or controversy because the common practice of putting the reserve or standby in system overhead increases the overhead. Planners must make sure that the people who use their reports do not add another standby item because they think they see an omission — i.e., no standby contained in system overhead — or use "overhead factors" containing standby costs. This matter is usually covered by stating that the system contains standby and detailing it in each situation — sometimes even extracting an estimate of its overall amount for information. This is another of the communications problems inherent in using a new technology.

Such an estimate can be made by totaling delay allowances and shop units as a percentage of total train time and then applying this percentage to total equipment inventory to obtain an equivalent standby inventory — repeating for emphasis: for information only.

The common practice of assuming that "public" or common-carrier equipment will be available for standby has some hazards. For one, it may commit the new system design to equipment that is interchangeable with common-carrier equipment. Since most of the undifferentiated fleet of common-carrier cars is badly obsolete, this is a serious and sometimes fatal flaw. Such compromises cost money. Incidentally, this is one of the compromises made by the power plant man who counted on resale of his coal cars if oil, gas or atoms should take over. It cost him money, too. In his *particular* case he would have been better off with a low-sophistication project to use low-budget secondhand cars, and he could have had his compromise, too, but not his status symbol consisting of expensive trains.

### 4.3.3 Whose Capital?

**It really makes no difference. Capital charges pay for rented money, regardless of where it is rented. "Profits" and other equity returns are residuals, in accordance with commercial realities.**

### 4.3.4 Leases

**Leases are all devices for borrowing money and must be so evaluated. A "full service" lease is a package deal involving two separate transactions — borrowing money and buying service. It must be regarded with the skepticism reserved for packages of dissimilar elements sold without itemization. Most leases are, in effect, mortgages, and lessees are expected to pay off in full even if the need for the tool ends — and when the tool is paid for, give it back.**

In sophisticated systems the business of servicing equipment is more economically performed at the new system's own facility than at the general-purpose facilities of a car company. Regardless of owners' claims, few if any car shops will be capable of even near-optimum provision of the services an integral train needs.

Integral train utilizations are beyond the expectations of most car companies. The car company's sales pitch is based on the premise that the user will pay for the car, completely, and leave the car company with a still-salable asset. Any suggestion that the lease pay for the car in the same time the car is consumed will elicit considerable disinterest. It is just as well to have this matter understood at the outset. It is just as well to make it clear that the usual mileage rates and rationale will not apply. Such formulas, applied to integral train utilizations, could enrich car companies at the expense of shippers *and* railroads. Unless car companies are the clients, this is *not* the idea.

In general, users will find it advisable to go to finance companies for financing and avoid tie-ins.

### 4.3.5  Time Bonus-Penalty Rates

**One hazard of using sophisticated train equipment is that its value depends on utilization, and railroads are often deficient in this respect. All the technology is directed to making it easy to move the train and inconvenient to stand it still. It is usually advisable to use a bonus-penalty clause as well. The bonus for early completion of a mission can be about 65% of the actual ownership cost. Time so gained can be sold, as available, at about 80% of "standard" rate. Delay penalties should be about 125% to 150% of the ownership costs. Accounts should be settled every trip, lest outstanding balances represent contingent liability, subject to massive and unscheduled claim if a railroad comes in late.**

A division superintendent can be allowed to claim time bonus only if he supplies a reliable estimated time of arrival (ETA) so that the next superintendent can call a crew. If he fails to do so, effective arrival time may be used. Correspondingly he must be charged for any initial terminal delay (ITD) he causes on the next division by not making or meeting his ETA.

Most integral train system schedules will contain considerable delay allowances -- often as much as 10% of total cycle time. If this time is allowed to accumulate, there will soon be no effective pressure on operating forces to bring the train in on time. Loss of money already earned but not yet realized will seldom motivate action. A parallel can be cited in the operation of car rental (per diem) as presently figured. Roads with per diem credit balances tend to become complacent.

Similarly a time-bonus will be only slightly effective in actually producing train time. The threat of time penalties will be more effective, and hence the basic schedule should not include all of the delay allowances used in designing the system and determining the amount of equipment to be provided.

### 4.3.6  Profits and Equity Returns

**Profit or equity return is payment for risk. It is a residual, left over after costs — including capital costs — are met. Many economic studies incorrectly include interest and capital recovery in something called "return on investment."**

### 4.4  Commercial Strategy

**A railroad planning an integral train system normally seeks a profit on transportation whether channeled directly or through equipment rentals. While planning for applications where the system *is* applicable it must protect itself against demands that integral trains be provided for shippers who cannot effectively use them. An impressive array of "gimmicks" will be encountered.**

Shuttles are easiest to plan and can be protected easily against misapplication, but the number of such opportunities is limited and some of the best opportunities are not in this group. For more complex services railroads are advised to encourage users to lease a train, part time if necessary, and run it as a shipper's train. This advice relates to railroads' vulnerability to inappropriate demands for "equitable" treatment which is not actually equitable — it is just made to look that way. Conceivably a railroad-sponsored train could be owned by a wholly owned leasing company, analogous to a refrigerator car company; but commercial potentials of this device are limited.

Given current societal relationships, the more usual case will arise when a shipper — or shipper group — plans an integral train system to reduce cost of carriage. Such planning will lead to proposals that shipper(s) and railroad(s) divide the savings that none can have separately. There is little potential in any but honest attempts to reduce costs and divide the savings.

Again given the realities of the relationships, it is safe to forecast that too many uninformed railroaders — and industry traffic men — will regard such a proposal as merely another gambit in the "cold war" on rates. In justice it must be noted that too many industrial traffic men — and railroaders — have made "gimmicks" of legitimate improvements.

> *For example:* One carrier man, offered an opportunity to negotiate a division of a saving, reported to his superiors, "They got some rig-a-jig so I guess we'll have to give them something." He never knew what it was. Nor cared.

Some rail executives will respond with "defensive rate cuts," defending themselves against change per se — what one man described as "the traumatic experience of ingesting a new idea." When a shipper hires the planner and so instigates the process he will usually take a defensive rate cut and go back for more. The savings are still there — the costs are the same and only the rate is lower. Some will propose nominal "unit train" tariffs that merely disguise rate cuts. All such schemes seek to avoid intellectual exercise, even for money. Such phenomena *must* eventually decline.

Various intellectual and technological intermediates will be offered — sometimes seeking efficiency but sometimes seeking only to avoid real change. They cannot be rejected out of hand, nor can they be taken, without analysis, at face value.

The often-asked question of exclusiveness — in the "monopoly" context — is easily answered. It is not practical for any shipper to have, for long, a conclusive advantage in any trade. Even if only one shipper can effectively use his own integral train, an enterprising railroad, leasing company or shipper co-op will come up with something that can compete — usually a jointly used integral train running on a still-bigger traffic base. Similarly there is little traffic that is "captive" for long. If a railroad with for-now-captive trade will not make the changes to obtain a share of the profit, the traffic can be lost to other competition — or to decentralization.

### 4.4.1 Attitudes and Objectives

Integral trains may be used for aggressive, defensive or competitive objectives. They can go out and get trade someone else has or they can seek new business. They can reduce costs in response to a threat — and sometimes a hold-the-line program can make just enough technological improvements to meet the threat and avoid the effort of going out after more profit — until the next crisis. Such a course of action is popular but irrational. Integral trains can be used competitively even where it is virtually certain that any improvement will be matched. In such cases — e.g., steel — every participant must keep trying lest an import or a competitive material or someone else take all their business.

An aggressive application can be defined as one designed to take traffic away from some other mode of transportation or some other railroad, or to obtain traffic that does not now move at all. The basic scheme is to use an integral train system to produce transportation at costs that make it profitable to offer rates that will be commercially conclusive. This practice is available in many situations, but only commercially oriented aggressive operators are likely to use it. For greatest profit the basic philosophy should be "How much can I do?", not "How little can I get away with?" To cite one reason — the greater the technological advance, the higher the entry price imitators face. Each man and each organization must decide which is his or its nature and interest. An attempt to interest a nonaggressive organization in an aggressive application will be a frustrating experience.

Defensive applications are numerous and various. In one group of cases the integral train alternative offers a clear case for better profits and lower rates — dividing the savings in the classic manner at the expense of wasteful practices. (The process of dividing the savings is rate-making.) However, there will be those who fear change, or fear — rightly or wrongly — exposure of their past inaction, and who therefore propose to defend themselves against change. Classically any improvement opportunity will seem like a personal affront to someone who "should" have made the change already. In such cases the characteristic response is to offer a rate cut, with or without a tariff change that superficially offers some justification, to get regulatory approval. In such cases the "convenience of the carrier" leads to doing the work in the way it was done before, and hence the same costs prevail.

Another defensive application is to make just enough technological change to make just enough savings to preserve a past actual or supposed profit level after granting whatever rate cuts the commercial realities make necessary. In such cases there remain opportunities for further savings by making further changes in technology. The planner of such a system typically shows some failure to understand why he should make more changes "just for more money — I held the line didn't I?" In fact, if the railroad instigates the change it is usually possible to get *all* the available improvements, in a single package, accepted by the shipper, with the same rate that could be had for a less economic technology.

In a competitive situation someone always suggests that all that is needed is to band together and deny any changes since sooner or later all competitors would have to make the improvements and none would gain at his competitors' expense. The fallacies of this view are obvious. Decentralization, imported goods and other whole industries are all available to customers and, anyway, cartels do not seem to hold together very well. Besides, if one moves fast he can get some money in before the competition catches up.

The large potentials available make the aggressive use more promising — in terms of money. But in the hands of a timid type, preoccupied with tradition, with minimizing exposure or with committeeing, no aggressive scheme can succeed.

## 4.4.2 "Captive" Trade

There is no such thing, for long. Anyone who thinks he has a captive trade is likely also to be of the type that resists change — even resisting more profit because that is a change, too. Such people are a real obstacle. The economic treatment for temporarily captive trade, for a railroad, is to install the new system and split the saving — not always evenly. (The shipper's collaboration is usually needed to install the physical changes associated with maximum profit.) For a shipper whose railroad is adamant, the treatment is to move the operation to some other plant. Adamant positions in such cases are not commercially sound, because the proposed changes are for savings to be divided. Such an adamant management is refusing money in an irrational manner and usually believes that all changes are "gimmicks" to take something from it.

There are many examples of "captive" trade that did not stay captive. A few examples will suffice.

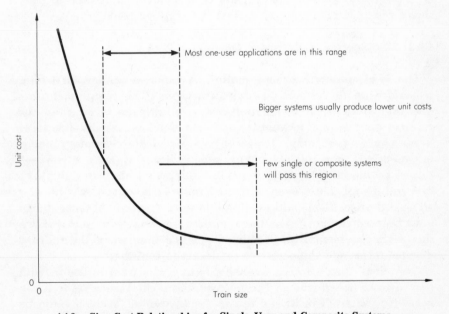

4.4.2 — Size-Cost Relationships for Single-User and Composite Systems

For any heirarchy of systems the unit cost will usually vary with train size as shown. There will be few occasions to test the right limb of the curve and many occasions to explore the left limb. The application of a large train — itself economic — to a small system that cannot keep it busy will test the right limb of the curve but will seldom survive economic analysis. In such cases the best correction is to combine systems to make a composite. For most systems a discontinuity (not shown) occurs when a second train is added. Its effect is to inhibit the use of more than one train per system except for compelling reasons. It takes a *very* big system to support two trains.

Minnesota once thought it had a monopoly on iron ore. It was necessary to show quite forcefully and at considerable cost that this was not the case.

Railroads thought they had a monopoly on energy transportation, and then the mine-mouth plant was invented.

As this is being written, railroads serving eastern utilities have announced a rate rise for coal. The largest affected utility had announced that in 10 years its coal burn would drop more than 60% — and then announced acceleration to about 18 months.

Many manufacturing enterprises have established plants in the South and West, near the newer markets, to avoid transportation costs.

Imports of steel for the automobile and pipeline businesses have been rising, in part because of disaffection with price and delivery of domestic steel.

In most cases unit costs will decline with volume, and hence there is an incentive to get more trade, thus destroying some of the already shaky rationale of protecting a small but captive trade.

### 4.4.3 The Specter of Exclusive Dealing

This is essentially a pricing matter. A common carrier must offer its services to all shippers on equivalent terms. This requirement was once thought to demand equal unit costs to all shippers or even that the railroad must absorb locational (and sometimes other) disadvantages — e.g., by cross-subsidy. However, more realistic regulatory determinations are now possible. For integral train systems a common carrier should file a tariff for running a shipper's train, using shipper's fuel and maintenance, over an agreed route on a agreed schedule for an agreed price. Some will quail at this word "agreed" because it suggests "agreed charges." For them, a thesaurus will help. Incidentally, this particular mental block is a relic of the time when the railroad dictated terms and shippers were expected to conform.

Once filed, such a rate is available to any who want to use it, with their own or leased trains. The railroad will seek all such trade it can get — for the profit in it; and this is the answer to "What if someone else wants the same service?"

Tariff rates for running such trains will consist of a substantial base price for the train with a small differential based on train size. The rate at all levels, and all increments in the rate, will be compensatory. The minimum rate for the minimum train will pay all pertinent railroad-incurred incremental costs and make a contribution to "overhead" and profit. The increase charged for increased train size will pay for increased railroad-incurred incremental costs and make a further contribution to overhead and profit.

Railroads will find, if such operations become popular, that their conventional services will decline in importance as traffic is diverted to integral trains. Such declines will not be as fast as the integral train growth, because much of the integral train business will be new traffic — traffic that would not move at all under conventional rates and practices. Integral trains will also divert to themselves existing traffic that otherwise would be lost entirely. And the productivity ratios are such that sharp reductions in capital commitments can be made.

*For example:* An integral train in one-way bulk traffic can achieve utilizations 15 to 20 times "conventional." In general cargo, utilizations can be 25 to 30 times "conventional." The resulting elimination of investments in new equipment can enable railroads to bring new equipment outlays almost to a stop if even a modest integral train revolution can be inspired.

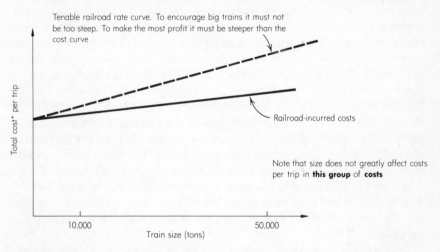

Tenable railroad rate curve. To encourage big trains it must not be too steep. To make the most profit it must be steeper than the cost curve

Railroad-incurred costs

Note that size does not greatly affect costs per trip in **this group** of **costs**

Total cost* per trip

10,000    50,000
Train size (tons)

*Incremental costs that **must** be included in railroad rates — per train **trip,** not per unit of freight. Total logistics costs vary more steeply

### 4.4.3 — Railroad-Incurred Cost Variation With Train Size

Those costs that *must* be in the railroad "rate" — i.e., crew, incremental track maintenance and similar items that must be performed by the railroad — will increase relatively little with train size — they are nearly the same for a 50,000-ton train as for a 10,000-ton train. Thus the cost per ton for the larger train is greatly less than for a smaller train, and larger sizes offer economic incentive meriting encouragement. It does not follow that other transportation-related costs will have such nearly level curves as these railroad-incurred costs. Railroads that quote integral train running rates by the ton will, in effect, deny themselves profits — the rate curve can be made steeper than the cost curve, but if it is too steep it will discourage the use of large trains, where the highest profits are. Use of per-ton rates and minimum sizes is a crude and eventually self-defeating makeshift.

Similarly such things as CTC installations diminish in importance as the number of trains decreases (with a few large units doing the work). Many lines can avoid costly new installations and eliminate maintenance on old ones made surplus. Similarly yards can be consolidated or eliminated and local trains can be abolished.

It is thus apparent that railroads have much to gain. But it is also apparent that these improvements are the kind that will cause adverse comment if improperly handled.

Therefore, to protect the gains and avoid the problems, railroads will be well advised to encourage train-leasing and the use of forwarders to serve small shippers, while themselves offering train-running tariffs for all.

### 4.4.4 Small Users

Once it is understood that an integral train need not be a shuttle, it is apparent that it can serve small users by trip leasing or using forwarders. Railroaders can no longer cross-subsidize to absorb small operators' disabilities when the large shippers can turn to private carriage — hence the traditional "small shipper protection" is no longer pertinent. When the large shipper "goes private," his traffic is not on the common carrier at all, and the small "protected" shipper has the burden of supporting the common carrier all by himself. So the small shipper benefits even when he is below the already-low integral train threshold of applicability — he is served by keeping the big shipper on the rails and so helping to keep the common carrier alive by any contribution that can be exacted from him. The use of an integral train wherever it is applicable maximizes the contributions to fixed costs — that is part of the definition of applicability — thus minimizing the demands made on the small shipper to whom the common carrier is essential.

Trip leasing will be an important device for serving medium-sized and small users. In this way many shippers large enough for sophistication but too small for one-user trains can be served. A variation will serve large-volume diverse-destination business. This last is illustrated by a potential system of continent-wide integral train general cargo movement. In such a system a regular schedule of integral container trains is used, over a few routes, serving a limited number of major market centers. The mainline movement is by integral train and the branchline operation is a local function in each area whether it is a truck, barge, local train, or whatever. Such a system is available to all and none can claim discrimination — the planning unit is a single container, with train space reserved like airplane seats.

The trains can either be common carriers or can be trip-leased, or a

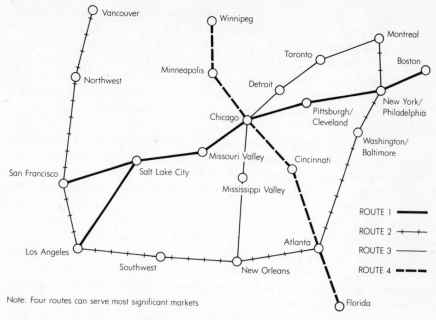

**4.4.4 — General Cargo System**

This sketch shows, schematically, one of several possible route and station schemes for an integral train container system. Movement beyond the gateways shown would be subject to competition among local carriers of all kinds, with local problems commercially isolated from the overall system.

composite system can be used with variations limited only by planners' ingenuity.

As integral train conversion proceeds, if it does, some attention to public education will be needed to get across the fact that even the smallest shipper, who cannot use an integral train system himself, benefits by keeping the large user on the system.

### 4.4.5 "Compromises"

Most of the compromises offered will be directed to noneconomic or antieconomic objectives, explainable only in terms of "personality problems." The most frequently encountered motive is to avoid change, often from real or imagined fears of criticism for past failure to make improvements that look (and are) simple. All such proposals should be subject to rigorous economic analysis. Few will survive but it is unwise to assume that none will. The most frequently encountered fallacy will be found in burdened or allocated costs.

Unit train schemes based on accumulating cars illustrate one compromise that costs more than what it replaces (they just "bunch" the cars). Such a scheme has already spent the money for the mine runs (or equivalent) and the intermediate yard — and that is where much of the money goes.

Similarly, some people point to the long coal trains on the N&W and claim that they are "unit trains." They are not — incidentally, a recent N&W annual report said that the average train size, before the merger brought in considerable noncoal trade, was smaller than 3,000 tons.

Similarly, others have claimed that the wheat movement of western Canada is a "unit train" operation because the lack of other trade in the region leaves little else to carry. What these people miss is that the essence of the new technology is to shorten the process, and none of these operations eliminates any steps or activities — particularly the expensive ones.

The fallacy of allocated costs in the economic area is conceptually matched by the fallacy of general-purpose equipment and standardized handling in the technological field. They both undertake to force dissimilar phenomena into a "standard" form. "Mission orientation" is now starting to gain acceptance, to displace "pattern orientation," and this development is encouraging.

## 4.5 Regulation

All railroads likely to be encountered are regulated common carriers, and some users — e.g., power companies — are also regulated. In general, any charge made for any service by a common carrier is a regulated rate and must meet these tests:

A — It must be nondiscriminatory — i.e., available to all on equivalent terms.

B — It must be compensatory — i.e., must pay its way and contribute to fixed costs.

Integral train systems planned as herein outlined will be profitable and hence compensatory. Once this is understood, railroads will hasten to sell them to all who will buy — and who can use them — hence they will be nondiscriminatory.

Regulators sometimes seek to "rig" rates to allocate markets. In other cases regulators assert that rates, collectively, should be as high as possible lest the collectivity of transportation companies receive less gross revenue than they otherwise might be able to extract from the public. This set of ideas only needs illumination in most cases for effective challenge.

Pragmatically, the best plan is to isolate as much as possible from regulatory concern by limiting the railroad's services to driving the trains — the rest is none of the regulators' business.

## 4.5.1 Nonregulated Elements

Most of the costs can be beyond regulators' scope. Train time cost is usually half the total cost, and for a shipper's train this cost is not subject to regulation. Similarly, fuel oil, train maintenance cost and the like are not part of the rate when the shipper supplies them. The only cost items *necessarily* in the regulated rate are:

A — Railroad train crews and their direct supervision
B — Incidental railroad labor
C — Incremental track maintenance
D — Liability for railroad negligence
E — Overhead, profit and other carrier markup; fixed by nego-
    tiation, not engineering

Items A to D are capable of reliable estimate.

Items A to D will usually be 10% to 25% of the total of all actual outlays (incremental costs) in an integral train system — and usually near the lower end of the range. When railroad "markup" is considered in relation to the part of railroad plant that is actually used for an integral train system, it will become apparent even to the most obtuse that the system is conceptually sound. The only remaining resistance will be from those who fear change per se or who have some real or imagined present advantage which might not survive scrutiny. One such family

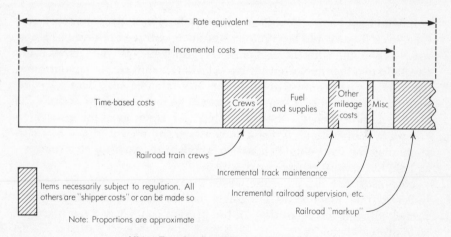

#### 4.5.1 — Regulated and Nonregulated Items

If trains are owned and managed by their users, the regulated common carrier furnishes relatively little of the service package. Regulators can be concerned only with those elements furnished by the regulated carriers in each situation. This concept is a step toward the original concept of the railroad as a public road on which each user supplies his own equipment — the concept of the highway today. The stereotyped bureaucratic response will lead regulators to attempt to intrude into other areas — egged on by shippers who do not want to take part in improvements or are about to lose artificial protections — and planners must help resist such efforts.

of resistances is found when considerable "other" traffic does not meet its incremental cost but no one dare admit the fact lest the "compensatory" criterion be applied according to law. The rationale of resisting the "goldfish bowl" economics of integral train systems in such cases is obvious. Regulators in such a case predictably respond to political pressure.

> *For example:* Canadian railroads have claimed that the politically untouchable Crows Nest grain rates are ruinously below cost. Yet technological change is resisted "to protect the present profit in grain hauling."

The common rationale of switching allowances illustrates the usual mental process. It says:

> A — A switching allowance may not be more than the patron actually spends to perform the service, and
> B — A switching allowance may not be more than it would cost the railroad to perform the service.

In theory the shipper who finds a way to make a saving is not supposed to get any of it. Of course this theory is not always applied as written. Commercially it is not sound, stable nor tenable. But planners must prepare each case to meet the obvious problems in this area.

### 4.5.2 "Monopoly"

**It would not be practical to sustain an effective shipper monopoly for long, even if one could be created. Railroads will seek to serve as many users as possible with the profitable integral train systems. Small users can band together and often secure even better unit costs than one giant user. While one route will be lower in attainable cost than all competitors, it is unlikely that its charges will be low enough to exclude the others, despite theory — unless the merger trend goes far enough to eliminate competition. Even if they were, the owner of the low-cost route may not have enough managerial talent to exploit it effectively — or hold his advantage once he has it.**

This discussion is part of the whole theory of monopoly. Experience indicates that monopolies inevitably fail to survive unless they are protected by government fiat. In the present context it is not intended so to protect them.

Therefore those who might claim that the effective use of an integral train system represents a trend to monopoly simply do not have their facts.

The argument goes something like this:

> A giant company can use an integral train and get its costs down. A small shipper cannot use the system. (Untrue.) The integral train economics are large enough to dominate in some

trades. (True.) Therefore those who do not use them — once anyone does — will suffer serious loss of markets. (True, but when the system is available to all, whose problem is that?) Another version goes this way:

But once we start using the system, and depending on the savings, the railroad will raise rates as high as it can. (Of course — doesn't everyone charge all he can get? Even the man who makes the complaint. But the integral train system, *where applicable*, can still be less costly than any other — that is the definition of applicable.)

### 4.5.3 Regulatory Criteria

**Budgeting is a "cost-plus" process which assures that rates are compensatory — until someone defines "compensatory" to cover a lot of the unrelated costs that are levied on railroads for "social" good and blanketed into railroad "costs." (That *does* happen.) In that case it can be said that a shipper on a fortunate line is alleged to be entitled to lower rates than one whose railroad is honored to provide a publicly needed commuter service somewhere. Once the rates are profitable, no railroad has any incentive to become discriminatory — it should want all it can get.**

The data on which regulatory decisions and policies are based usually leave much to be desired.

*For example:* A book came to this writer's desk which purported to state the actual, direct cost per car of moving freight in each region of the United States. An appendix reported the amount of passenger deficit included in the "direct" cost of moving freight on selected lines. The book went immediately to the "circular file."

Of course this family of ideas can be argued the other way, too.

*For example:* A railroad used freight profits to finance a local suburban commuter deficit and each month announced the figures that showed the results. Eventually the freight business declined — home building drove industry out — the freight profit just was not there anymore and commuters were asked to pay their way. Irate commuter groups demanded that the line get up the money somewhere — they would not "see their fares raised just to make up what the freight business no longer earned."

And there is still another side to this one.

A state regulatory agency seriously claimed that a commuter living on a line owned by a large and prosperous system was "entitled" to better service than a commuter living on a line

owned by a small, local railroad. Of course the shippers pay
the bill but they are "rich corporations far away."

It is apparent that regulatory criteria are not always rational. Integral train planners must simply document the case, insist on recognition of the facts, resist attempts to becloud them, and patiently work for rational treatment.

One of the more startling in recent years is found in 1967 Canadian transport legislation. It says:

> In "monopoly" cases a fair "rate" is direct cost plus 150%, but it does not define direct cost nor does it provide for even finding out whether management is seriously exploiting available technology to improve direct cost. Such formulas are inapplicable to integral train systems because the definition of the service package is different from that assumed by the formula writers — and for other reasons.

### 4.5.4   Market "Protection"

**The most serious regulatory problems will arise when rail rates are used to enforce effective market allocations, as in a cartel. Then it is the transportation economies themselves that will be under attack — especially when shippers price but do not ship by rail.**

The economics of integral train technology cannot affect all shippers uniformly (few technological changes do so — in any industry), and they often operate to eliminate historic high rate barriers that protect inefficient but often vocal operators. If the commitment to a functional, even if formless or informal, cartel is too deep, the search for transportation economy is pointless, by integral trains or in any other way except by private carriage. Someone often says:

> But if costs go down, sooner or later rates will go down and then our relative positions will change. This, too often, from *shippers.*

And the least efficient — who need rigged rates — are the most vocal. Perhaps there is a causal relationship.

# APPENDIX A
# NEXT-GENERATION EQUIPMENT

This brief review is intended to suggest directions in which integral train equipment can evolve. All the needed technology is now available, though there are few places where it can be had all in one place. There are some basic patents involved but none are believed to be held for obstructionist purposes. The principal obstacle is intellectual inertia. Realization of the savings that new equipment can bring must wait for some project large enough to cover the development cost on the first sale, or until some vendor of equipment chooses to offer the new hardware for the profit in it. The potential is considerable.

## A-1 Basic Premises

Certain basic improvements merit attention — and some are obviously more promising than others.

### A-1.1 Tare Weight Economy

Contemporary (1967) locomotives weigh nearly 200 lbs. per *usable* horsepower and there is little that can be done about it — in present technology. At economic integral train power ratios 1 horsepower is used for 700 to 1,000 lbs., of which 200 is in the locomotive. So long as the train uses a separable locomotive, the locomotive must be heavy for traction.

The integral train with its controlled consist can use payload for ballast — and hence can use low-powered axles for slip-control and can exploit low-tare engines.

For example, a gas turbine and geared drive, assembled of transportation-designed (not aircraft) components, weighs about 5 to 6 lbs. per horsepower. If the total load of 700 to 1,000 lbs. per horsepower remains constant, the payload-car combination can rise by 195 lbs., from about 500-800 to 700-1,000 lbs. This represents a large increase in earning capacity — 25% to 40%. The low-tare drive systems can be had at *less* cost than the conventional diesel-electrics. All that remains lacking is an entrepreneurial type or a big project to exploit them. It will be a sound case even when the "administered" price of diesel-electrics comes down.

Similarly, car tare weight merits attention. Present AAR specifications effectively forbid (not directly but by use of arbitrary rigidity requirements) the efficient use of the newer (since 1910) steel alloys. Controlled consists permit lighter structures for integral trains by reducing the demands made on them — no humping, limited slack, no "bonfire" thawing, no door abuse, for example.

It does not follow that the new cars will be built of light metal but it does follow that they will be designed for low tare. An example is found in bottom gate selection for bulk cars. A long, narrow clamshell gate must span a considerable length (8 to 20 feet) under load, whereas a drop-type latched gate has a shorter span (2 feet) and uses less structure. Similarly, the new cars can have their couplers and center-sill extensions replaced by simple (or internally cushioned) drawbars pinned at truck centers — eliminating considerable metal in each car, in part by eliminating transverse bending forces on curves.

Detail design would be inappropriate here but the direction of design philosophy is obvious.

### A-1.2 Reliability

Integral train cars can be run 700 to 900 miles per day or about 300,000 miles per year. Over a 10-year amortization period such cars will run 3,000,000 miles — about six times the lifetime mileage of most present cars. Reliability and longevity are both involved. Reliability is almost a wholly new subject in the railroad hardware business and offers one of the most promising areas for improvement. Longevity is a familiar concept — in years — but it is new in terms of service cycles.

The controlled nature of integral train service will greatly help here, too. The short life (in years) to limit exposure to corrosion and aging will also help. Presently attainable subsystems — sealed bearings, single-acting brakes without levers, adjusters and gadgets, absence of couplers, and even the very act of *designing* the cars (few present cars were designed; they just evolved) — will all help. But the surface of the problem of reliability design will barely be dented, even in the next generation of cars.

### A-1.3 Capital Procurement

The high utilizations will help to finance new gear. For example, a fleet of 18 conventional 70-ton coal cars can be sold "on the hoof" (for junk) for about $13,000 to $14,000. This is about enough to buy the one new, sophisticated-design car that can do all their work and have some capability margin, too. The technological lag is phenomenal when existing gear can be sold for junk for enough to buy the new. What is missing is the development and entrepreneurial spirit in an industry that simply does not innovate from within.

### A-1.4 Longevity Design

Designers' emphasis will be on longevity in terms of work done, not in terms of elapsed time.

For example: One car vendor asserted that he would not quote on a car intended to be "used up before it rusts out." He said "Yes, I read the specification, but I assumed and will continue to assume that what you really want is a car that will still be around for 30 years no matter how clearly you say otherwise."

The fact is that money spent on longevity in terms of time cannot, in its very nature, produce returns until many years have passed; but improvements designed to make the car perform reliably throughout its life will pay profits almost at once. This condition rules out all heavy designs and most "gadgets." The differential investments fail to meet a criterion calling for rapid capital recovery, and such criteria will be almost universal because:

A — Fast-recovery opportunities compete for capital and

B — There is a risk of obsolescence.

## A-1.5 Fuel

It is likely that hydrocarbons will continue to supply energy for a long time to come. The low unit cost of coal is a challenge to its economic use, but there is no way presently in sight to use it effectively. The low unit cost of liquified natural gas is also a challenge to its use, but that seems at least several years off. The prospect of using residual or crude oil economically is also some time off. The use of high-energy distillates in gas turbines is immediately feasible. The importance of tare weight may yet lead to the development of economic exotic fuels and engines to use them economically.

## A-2 Cars

Cars, in this context, are vehicles that carry the freight, though in the integral train of the future the car and the locomotive will no longer be distinct entities, nor separable pieces.

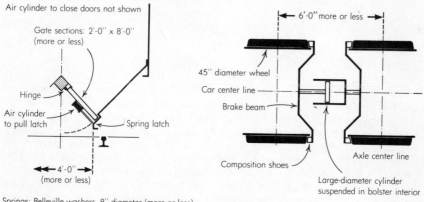

LONGITUDINAL SEGMENTED GATE   See also 2.2.3

BRAKE

### A-2 — Car Specialties

This sketch shows, in general scheme, the direct-acting brake and low-cost door that are suggested for the next generation of cars. The direct-acting brake can use one large cylinder on each truck and low air pressure, or a small cylinder and high pressure — but it needs a high air manifold to supply plentiful air as a substitute for adjustment gear and multiplying levers. It can be used only with composition shoes on 100-ton cars — clasp brakes are too heavy, complex and costly. The cylinder can be suspended within the bolster, carried on its end rods and on the brake beams, which in turn can be carried in slots on the truck sideframes in fixed relationship to the wheels. The doors shown use short-span panels closed by air and opened by gravity (once the latch is pulled by air). The slide slope sheets terminate in a flange detail that offers stiffness and permits using a gasket for fine materials.

## A-2.1 Bulk Cars

"Bulk" cars will carry commodities that move in trainload lots. Most small-volume "bulk" — carload goods — such as chemical intermediates, nonferrous concentrates, mineral specialties—e.g., bentonite—and the like will move in containers in which they can be loaded without further packaging.

### A-2.1.1 Gates

Bulk cars will almost certainly use center-hinged, center-dump longitudinal gate styles. To minimize tare and complexity the gates will probably be variations of drop bottoms with air latches, gasketed for most material. Such variant types as clamshells and spiral sectors will be used for special purposes — e.g., the spiral sector, sill-less bottom is virtually mandatory for scrap — but most bulk cars will not be *that* special.

### A-2.1.2 Trucks

Most bulk traffic, with the possible exception of Canadian wheat, will "load heavy," up to 65,000 lbs. per axle. Trucks will be weldments employing low-cost, high-reliability components — some of them patented. They will use oversize wheels, simplified brakes, and contoured disk (Belleville) springs with the basic objective of minimizing the number of vulnerable parts.

### A-2.1.3 Bodies

Bulk cars will use steep slopes and fillets and usually covers, insulation and body heat. The materials used will be high alloys, clad plates and the like to minimize tare weight and permit clean, fast unloading. Light metal vendors may be able to close the gap, in due time, one way or another, but at this writing steel seems to offer the best *potential* (and the poorest exploitation of it). There is no justification of such primitive practices as bare cars that have to have the ice chipped out of them or which require slow, costly and damaging unloading systems. Heat will be supplied by metal tape resistance elements applied to the entire outer surface and powered by a d.c. train bus to prevent freezing, not to thaw frozen loads, and plate or liner material selections will permit prompt discharge.

### A-2.2 Container Cars

All that is not bulk as above defined is here defined as container freight. Some research indicates that even autos are best handled by loading them on 80-foot bilevel racks that are then handled like containers, leaving the car itself completely general among general cargo elements.

Emerging container systems are all based on multiples of 20 feet long and 8 feet wide. (Heights can vary from pallets to 10 feet.) Such containers are coming to be known as ISA (International Standards Association) standard units suitable to rail, truck and marine use. Such an arrangement leads to a car with an 80-foot skeleton deck.

### A-2.2.1 Bodies

Container car bodies will undoubtedly be simple skeletons with cross-members for ISA standard boxes. There seems to be little long-term future to piggybacking, once a sophisticated integral container train system gets under way (or even sooner in many areas). The attainable economics point toward side transferring — for which there is existing hardware. Crane and turntable systems do not survive independent economic analysis when best-attainable schemes are compared.

### A-2.2.2 Trucks

An 80-foot car can theoretically carry 80 tons of payload (plus the containers). However, it is unlikely that an actual load of 80 tons can be attained, consistently at least. When the car is skeletonized and the tare weight is reduced as much as the structural considerations permit, the cars can use nominal 70-ton trucks and still have a capacity margin.

As in the case of bulk cars, trucks should be weldments, designed specifically for the task. Direct-acting brakes, truck-center pinned (solid or internally cushioned) drawbars, and other refinements should be used. For container trains it is likely that 33-inch wheels — usually loaded at about 50,000 lbs. per axle or less, and only occasionally as heavy as 55,000 lbs., will become standard.

### A-2.2.3 Transfer Units

It is likely that common trailer trucks adapted to side transfer (one or two containers at a time) will be developed to a high degree of refinement, with a line of accessories (presently available in large part) that will adapt the container to a wide variety of industrial situations. For in-station use a rubber-tired container transfer unit capable of handling four loaded containers at a time (or four pallets loaded with pipe or structurals) — a 90-ton, 80-foot trailer truck — will emerge. It will be less costly to switch containers than to switch cars, and shippers located where the giant truck can reach them will enjoy a locational advantage, so forwarders and some industries will seek locations next door to the stations.

### A-3 Motive Power

Power development will tend to better tare weight and, secondarily, to better fuel efficiency — as noted above, large improvements are available now. As with all other equipment, the power systems that succeed will be the ones that need least maintenance and offer the best reliability (not unrelated, obviously). Ideally the unit will be installed and forgotten except for "formal" regulator-required "inspections" which amount to little more than paying for a timecard. Among presently available systems the small (700-to-1,000-hp.) gas turbines closely approach this requirement, with turbo-electrics rather far behind — but not hopelessly so.

### A-3.1 Electric Transmissions

Systems based on large power generating units will use electric transmissions. Such systems are exposed to the problems of electrical gear — recent past experience has been somewhat less than ideal in the matter of electric traction and transmission reliabilities, though the interurbans of another day seemed to perform reliably.

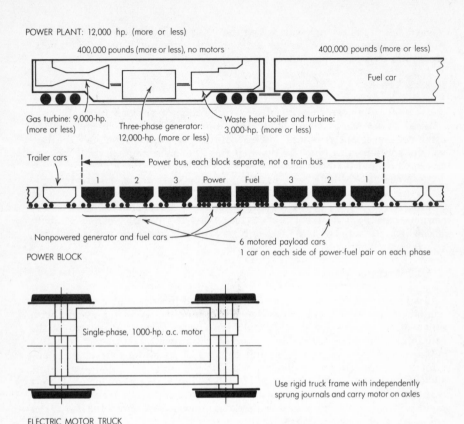

POWER PLANT: 12,000 hp. (more or less)

400,000 pounds (more or less), no motors          400,000 pounds (more or less)

Fuel car

Gas turbine: 9,000-hp.
(more or less)          Three-phase generator:          Waste heat boiler and turbine:
12,000-hp. (more or less)          3,000-hp. (more or less)

Trailer cars          ←——— Power bus, each block separate, not a train bus ———→

1     2     3     Power     Fuel     3     2     1

Nonpowered generator and fuel cars          6 motored payload cars
POWER BLOCK          1 car on each side of power-fuel pair on each phase

Single-phase, 1000-hp. a.c. motor

Use rigid truck frame with independently
sprung journals and carry motor on axles

ELECTRIC MOTOR TRUCK

### A-3.1 — Gas Turbine-Electric Power Block

This scheme is feasible only with bulk trains on which the loads will be all about alike
and the *whole train* is loaded or empty (with equal loads no individual motor controls
are needed.) A generating station is used, carried aboard a power car designed to limit
unproductive tare and make the maximum capacity available for equipment. The
transmission is electric, using a balanced three-phase distribution to 24 motored axles,
mechanically coupled in pairs to limit slip. Brake grids should be rigged to simulate
a failed motor until the train returns home, to eliminate the need for elaborate individual controls.

### A-3.1.1 Generating Plants

It seems feasible to install about 12,000 hp. on a six-axle, specially designed
nonmotored power car and to carry enough fuel for a reasonable cycle in a
specially designed six-axle tank car. Such a unit will use a standard 8,000-
kw. utility-type three-phase generator overloaded to about 9,000 kw. (a
short — 50,000-hr. — life in utility terms). It will be powered by a large gas
turbine on one end and a waste-heat steam turbine on the other end to produce an acceptable fuel rate and exhaust temperature. The power and tank
cars will be unmotored in the interest of control simplicity and to maximize
useful load.

Plant electrical output will be used to drive electric motors on the three adjacent payload cars on each side, at about 500 hp. per axle. It is likely that there will soon be a 1,000-hp. motor available that can be geared to two axles and mounted between the axles of a truck — to serve motor economy, control simplicity and slip control.

### A-3.1.2 Controls

Such a system will use dynamic braking. It will use simple controls — especially in a bulk train, where all motored cars of a group are loaded identically. In that case the motors can be balanced on the three phases of the system with provision for using braking grids to simulate a failed motor until the unit can be serviced. In this way the controls can be rudimentary and individual motor control is not needed.

Such a system can be used only in a large train so that low-load operation of the gas turbine can be avoided — the large turbines are quite inefficient at low loads. In a large train, low power is provided by using some of the units at full power. It takes, for example, 25,000 to 40,000 tons of train to use six such units, and small trains so powered will be uneconomic.

Accessories in such trains will be powered from a d.c. train bus, independently supplied from one or more small gas turbines. The units intended for automotive use are adequate, when used with suitable generators, and the large units need not be used for minor loads. Further, it will probably be impractical to use a power bus on the train (too much copper), further supporting the need for a separate auxiliary system.

### A-3.1.3 Applicability

This system is probably limited to bulk trains. There will be too little space on the container trains for auxiliaries, the small wheels will limit the space available for motors, and the varying loads will make it difficult to assure identical or nearly identical loading of motored axles in each group.

In the bulk trades this system will permit the use of power blocks and trailer blocks to be assembled for specialized services in various ways. Since the bulk trades will tend to be specialized, this capability will be of more value in bulk than in container services.

### A-3.2 Mechanical Transmission Types

Mechanical transmission types become practical only with the development of a small, low-cost gas turbine suited to high-intensity, low-maintenance, high-performance vehicle use. Such a unit is now ready for commercial exploitation and is commercially available, though its vendor has not seen fit to solicit railroad trade — and others are reportedly on the way.

### A-3.2.1 Engines

The system uses 700- to 800-hp. engines, each geared to the two axles of one truck. Train power is controlled by regulating the number of engines in use — each requires a simple on-off control with little or no means of regulating its individual power output. Such engines can be installed at a rate of two per car, on two cars per block — one on each side of a tank car. On bulk trains they can be installed under the end slopes. On container cars they can be installed in an enclosure that simulates a container, one geared to the truck below and the other geared by a line shaft to the remote truck on the same car. Train control demands systematically diversified sequencing to avoid depleting individual tanks before completing a mission or to avoid bringing all engines in a system to scheduled overhaul at one time.

A variation would use two small engine compartments, one on each end of a powered car.

### A-3.2.2 Brakes

Systems of this kind will not use dynamic brakes unless some way is found for economically reversing the engine unit and modulating its reversal. This possibility should not be ruled out, but for the present it seems likely that the train will be reversed by means of gears controlled for a whole train, and dynamic brakes will not be used.

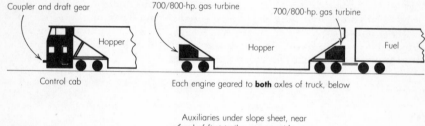

Coupler and draft gear     700/800-hp. gas turbine     700/800-hp. gas turbine

Hopper

Hopper

Fuel

Control cab       Each engine geared to **both** axles of truck, below

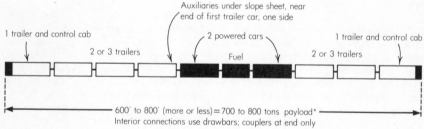

Auxiliaries under slope sheet, near end of first trailer car, one side

1 trailer and control cab     2 powered cars     1 trailer and control cab

2 or 3 trailers     Fuel     2 or 3 trailers

← 600' to 800' (more or less)=700 to 800 tons payload* →
Interior connections use drawbars; couplers at end only

Car count varies with car size, grades, speed, etc. Design around available engines

Alternate: Assemble blocks in pairs and omit interior end cabs

*100-ton cars, where roadway permits, will permit economy of space, tare and cost. Arrangement shown is for nominal 70-ton cars (e.g., for Canadian prairies)

### A-3.2-A — Nonelectric Bulk Train Block

One self-contained bulk car block will use four small (700- to 800-hp.) gas turbines, each driving a truck mechanically and drawing fuel from a tank car. Each block will also include suitable trailer cars and a cab at each end. The blocks can then be assembled into trains like subway cars. For instance a 50,000-ton (payload) train of nominal 70-ton cars (for the low-standard tracks of the Canadian prairies) to handle wheat will be close to 8 miles long (about 65 blocks including under-load allowance) and will be a formidable transportation machine. The engines used should be selected for industrial applicability, and converted (or misapplied) aircraft machines do not seem optimum nor perhaps even acceptable.

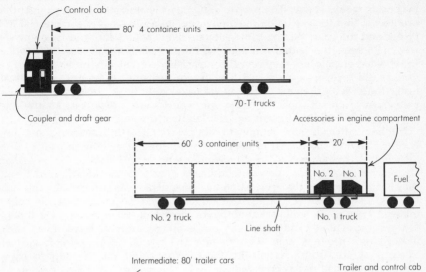

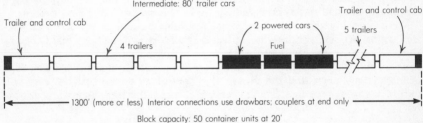

1300' (more or less) Interior connections use drawbars; couplers at end only

Block capacity: 50 container units at 20'

### A-3.2-B — Nonelectric Container Train

Each block of this train uses four small gas turbine engines, each driving one truck mechanically and drawing fuel from a tank car. A block will also contain trailer cars and have a control cab at each end, the whole arranged so that blocks can be assembled like subway cars to make trains. One block capable of handling containers totaling 1,000 feet (nominal 1,000 tons or 50 ISA units of 20 feet each), as indicated, will be widely suitable. Trains comprising as many as 30 to 35 such blocks will be found economical and applicable in many situations.

## A-3.2.3 Accessories

Trains so arranged will use separately powered electric (d.c.) bus systems for driving accessories such as compressors, lights, starters, heat, controls, etc.

### Addendum

The reader may be interested in a more or less popular-understanding description of the purpose and potential of integral trains which John G. Kneiling wrote for the January 1968 issue of TRAINS Magazine (© Kalmbach Publishing Co. 1967). Entitled "The Next Breakthrough: The True Train," it is reproduced here with the permission of the magazine:

Shipper-oriented research into transportation most often leads to the finding that if the proper equipment were for sale, startling reductions in transport costs would ensue. The proper equipment *is* capable of being built; the problem is that those who do the innovating do not have any commercial interest, and the users do not know enough about potentials to insist on progress. (Passenger-oriented rail men tell me the same about passenger cars.) In repeated encounters they reveal a surprising consistency in what they regard as the "proper equipment." The design turns out to be nearly identical every time. With the new tools, rail carriage could be so cheap that it would restore the railroad monopoly. No one would even think of trucking long distance or of building a plant on an inland waterway.

Neither railroads nor equipment builders in North America show any familiarity with the notion of progress in equipment or how to use it. One "Product Development" Vice-President spent a half day telling me that change *per se* was not allowed in railroad gear. To the last man of them, they seem convinced that perfection has been achieved; and patrons can just fit their business to the equipment offered. A large opportunity is being missed. The case is reminiscent of that of the diesel in the 1930's. Old-timers like me recall that to the last man the teakettle builders went down with flags flying, "proving" that the new machine was a fad — useful in special cases, if at all. Characteristically the new machine was introduced by a company that had not been significantly in the railroad business before.

We are now engaged in a search for a similar builder of the next-generation trains. We will continue to contact carbuilders, but we have few expectations. The new gear will probably have to come from a new (or foreign) source; but when it comes, it will have a conclusive competitive edge. The economics are such that the owner of a fleet of *new* conventional cars will find it advantageous to sell them for scrap when the new trains are offered for sale.

### The Equipment

The new equipment will consist of self-propelled *car blocks with a cab at each end* of every block. Each block will be made up of *either* container cars or bulk cars (with perhaps a few variations such as piggyback and short, heavy "steel" cars). Each block will carry a tank car and four gas turbines (using payload for ballast) and will eliminate electric drives.

The most promising block size will have a capacity of about 1000 tons with a maximum tare of 400 tons, including fuel for a week or more. The blocks will be used in very long trains. Each such train will carry *either* general or bulk cargo and run over the railroad on a mission-completion basis instead of an undifferentiated "flow of traffic" rationale.

Each block will be propelled by 3000 horsepower in four turbines (developed for ground transport service), each one geared directly to the two axles of one truck. All bulk cars will be covered and heated, and all will be stainless-steel lined and filleted for fast, clean unloading in motion. "Bulk" will mean trainloads, not carloads. Such goods as cement and nonferrous concentrates will move in containers. A tank container will be a variant, and later will come a tank train that can stop pipeline expansion cold.

The new trains will include systems for sequencing engines in a train. A 30-block container train will be 7 to 8 miles long and will carry 120 engines in addition to 30 auxiliary sets for train heat, refrigerator motors, compressors, and lights. The speed of the train will be controlled by a combination of throttling and controlling of the number of engines being run.

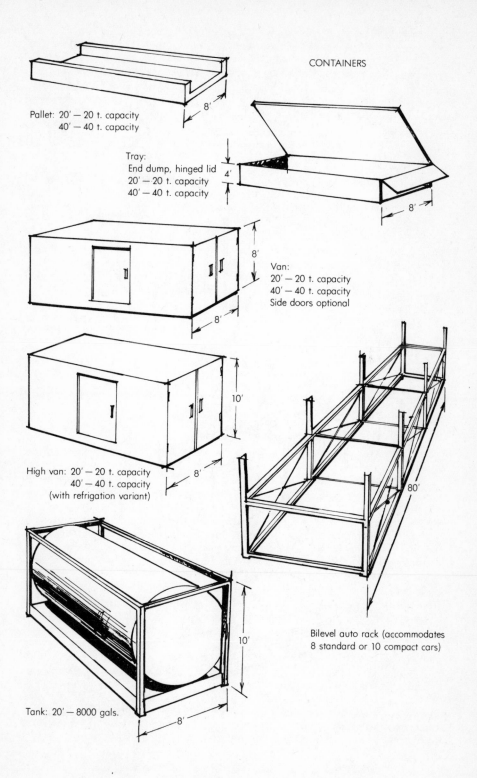

CONTAINERS

Pallet: 20' — 20 t. capacity
40' — 40 t. capacity

Tray:
End dump, hinged lid
20' — 20 t. capacity
40' — 40 t. capacity

4'

8'

Van:
20' — 20 t. capacity
40' — 40 t. capacity
Side doors optional

8'

8'

High van: 20' — 20 t. capacity
40' — 40 t. capacity
(with refrigation variant)

10'

8'

80'

Bilevel auto rack (accommodates
8 standard or 10 compact cars)

Tank: 20' — 8000 gals.

10'

8'

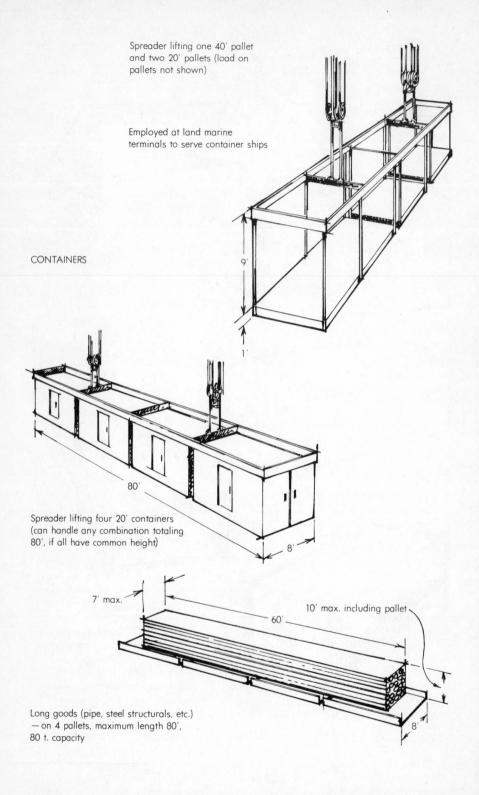

Spreader lifting one 40' pallet
and two 20' pallets (load on
pallets not shown)

Employed at land marine
terminals to serve container ships

CONTAINERS

9'

1'

80'

8'

Spreader lifting four 20' containers
(can handle any combination totaling
80', if all have common height)

7' max.

10' max. including pallet

60'

Long goods (pipe, steel structurals, etc.)
— on 4 pallets, maximum length 80',
80 t. capacity

8'

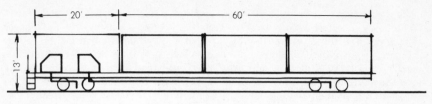

POWERED CONTAINER CAR

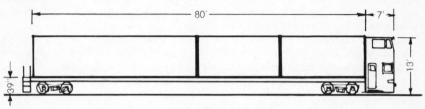

CAB-END CONTAINER CAR

Even in their first generation, the new trains will have many simple but novel mechanical features intended to produce high reliability and high performance. By comparison, the conventional car is a pile of junk. The new equipment will employ *truck-center articulation* with long drawbars, except at block ends. This will eliminate most separable couplers, brake connections, draft gear, and center sill extensions. The transverse forces on curves will be applied at trunk centers, reducing tare, bending stresses, maintenance, and wheel wear.

Mechanical design philosophy is exemplified in the brake system. If conventional train performance is regarded as standard, the new trains, with their electropneumatic system, pressure-maintained tanks, direct action, elimination of lever systems, and high-air manifold, can give the needed performance (stopping distance, slide control, and smoothness) with brakes on only a portion of the wheels. In the interest of reliability, however, redundant (*i.e.*, surplus) brakes should be provided so that above-standard performance can be achieved even with some of the elements out of service.

Bulk cars will be needed in 70-ton and 100-ton nominal sizes. Tare reduction inherent in a sophisticated design permits actual payloads to exceed the nominal without increasing total loads. Bulk cars will be equipped with trough hatches and power-closing, gravity-opening longitudinal bottom gates hinged to a diamond center sill with air-release latches. The design will provide for unloading at about 10,000 tons per hour, with the train serving as the feeder for a conveyor.

Container cars will be about 80 feet long to carry up to four 20-foot units per train, including pallet multiples for long goods. The powered container car will have a 60-foot deck and an engineroom.

There will be some system accessories — and all sales will be of *systems*. Bulk will be loaded and discharged through cone-and-crater bins, usually covered, with high-volume conveyors designed around the time value of trains — the logistics theme. This theme says that total cost is the design criterion, and let the policy men divide the savings. And equipment *does* have a time value.

Container service requires two accessories. One is a rubber-tired transfer truck — a giant tractor-trailer capable of side-transferring 80 feet of containers (80 tons net and containers) at one time. Such a rig is not an innovation — smaller ones are now in service. It will be an off-road device, used normally in a station and adjoining industrial property to tackle the jobs the switch engine costs so much to do. With this tool containers can be switched more cheaply than cars can be switched on a railroad — faster, too. The other container accessory is a convertible spreader beam for use in a container crane — such as at shipside — capable of handling four 20-foot units, or the equivalent, at a time. It will be a descendant of present spreaders. Lift truck, straddle carrier, gantry, and similar systems have proved uneconomic — unless you sell them.

The new trains will be made up of blocks, like subway trains. The train can be driven from any cab — but it will be a *train*, not a fleet of cars. No longer will the yardmaster make trains — no more yardmaster and no more yard. The design "philosophy" will be that of a lightweight, high-perform-

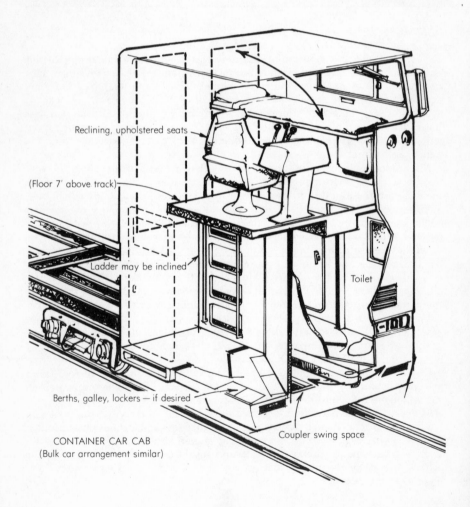

Reclining, upholstered seats

(Floor 7' above track)

Ladder may be inclined

Berths, galley, lockers — if desired

Toilet

Coupler swing space

CONTAINER CAR CAB
(Bulk car arrangement similar)

ance, and fast-amortization outfit. The trains should run up to 3 million miles in 10 to 12 years, then be replaced by something better.

The new gear will be used first for sophisticated traffic (there will soon be little else). The container versions will run only between a relatively small number of stations. At each station, an adjoining industrial park will offer distributors an inexpensive terminal service using the big transfer rigs. Others will get their freight by container truck at locally prevailing rates. Switchers, branch lines, and the like must go; since the time when these were essential to rural access, the truck and highway have been invented.

The new bulk train can gather wheat from country elevators or layer-load mixed coal from neighborhood mines cheaper than any other system. In the process, a full bulk train of upwards of 25,000 tons will visit each shipper in turn and pause while he discharges his bin into his assigned car(s) — which incidentally produces a designed blend at unloading. A carload of anything — e.g., coal — to one user is considered a container job.

From large bulk points, such as coal or potash mines or iron-ore preparation plants, the cheapest and best method employs a cone-and-crater bin with flood-feed units up to multiples of 10,000 tons per hour to load full trains up to 50,000 tons — or larger. Incidentally, this scheme can drive the barges and Lakers out of business. The 15 billion ton-miles per week now sold can theoretically be handled with 3000 car blocks, and not at very high speeds. This many blocks, plus a few more for misscheduling, can be bought for what the industry spent on cars alone in 1966 — and the new car block price includes power.

One effect of this idea is to bring more traffic — new and from other modes. It will also hasten abandonment of branches and urban-area switching operations. The conversion can be as complete as the steam engine displacement; it is trading on even more years of technological neglect.

With the new tools in operation, the railroad equipment of this continent will consist of a few thousand — perhaps as many as 5000 — of the new car blocks. Each will be a package of sophisticated equipment that is never al-

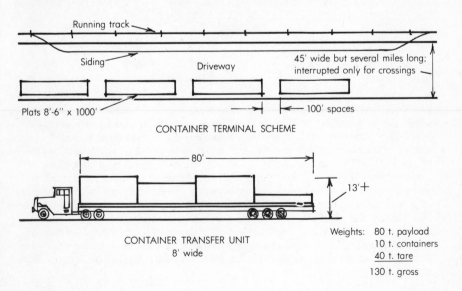

Running track

Siding

Driveway

45' wide but several miles long; interrupted only for crossings

Plats 8'-6" x 1000'

100' spaces

CONTAINER TERMINAL SCHEME

80'

13'+

CONTAINER TRANSFER UNIT
8' wide

Weights: 80 t. payload
10 t. containers
40 t. tare
130 t. gross

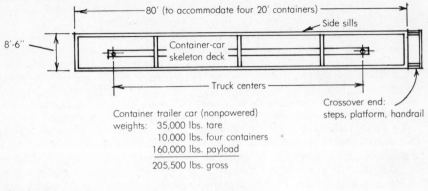

80' (to accommodate four 20' containers)

Side sills

8'-6"

Container-car
skeleton deck

Truck centers

Crossover end:
steps, platform, handrail

Container trailer car (nonpowered)
weights: 35,000 lbs. tare
10,000 lbs. four containers
160,000 lbs. payload
205,500 lbs. gross

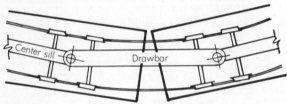

Center sill

Drawbar

TRUCK-CENTER ARTICULATION

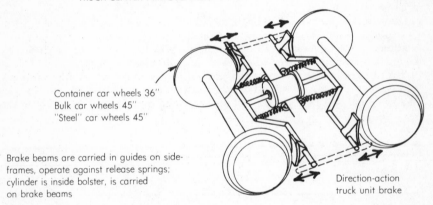

Container car wheels 36"
Bulk car wheels 45"
"Steel" car wheels 45"

Brake beams are carried in guides on sideframes, operate against release springs;
cylinder is inside bolster, is carried
on brake beams

Direction-action
truck unit brake

lowed out of its owner's control. They will run in long trains, on fixed schedules and routes, with peripheral functions performed by truckers.

It follows that secondary lines, most second track, and most signal systems will go. One train on the road for every 600 or so miles of track, after cutting to about 50,000 track-miles, does not need much control except a man with a voice radio. High utilization and high standards of preventive maintenance will eliminate most en route inspections and most servicing facilities except at a few new terminals. The new cars cost money, but conventional cars cost money too. In fact, the capital per ton of static capacity will be about the same as for conventional cars and engines. Conventional accounting, however, conceals this cost and thus frustrates its control — hence the "new" preventive maintenance, central dispatching, and elimination of en route servicing.

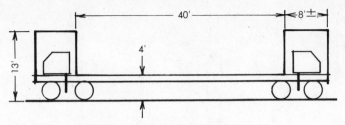

POWERED 100 t. CAPACITY "STEEL" CAR

40' deck, 100 t. capac. "steel" car
(for ingots, slabs, plates, etc.)
weights:   30,000 lbs. tare
            3,000 lbs. pallet and fastenings
          230,000 lbs. load
          263,000 lbs. gross

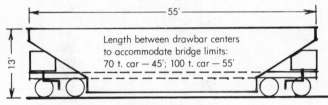

Length between drawbar centers
to accommodate bridge limits:
70 t. car — 45'; 100 t. car — 55'

POWERED BULK CAR

Trailer car (nonpowered) tare weights:
40,000 lbs. for 100 t. capacity
35,000 lbs. for 70 t. capacity

(100 t. capacity cars shown; 70 t. variant possible)

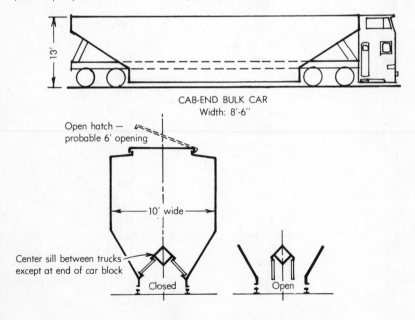

CAB-END BULK CAR
Width: 8'-6"

Open hatch —
probable 6' opening

10' wide

Center sill between trucks
except at end of car block

Closed                    Open

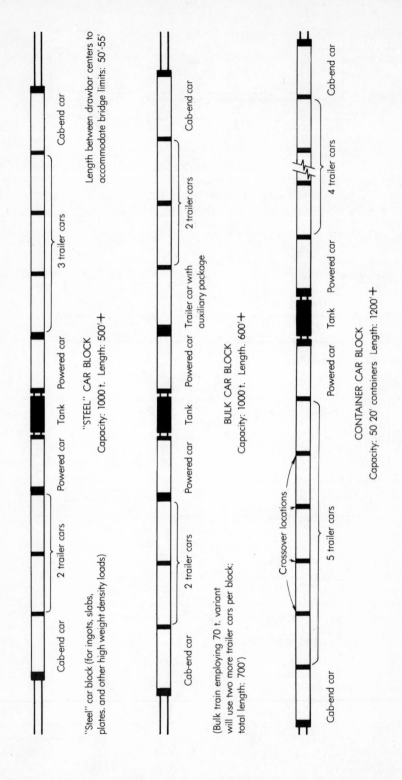

Cab-end car    2 trailer cars    Powered car    Tank    Powered car    3 trailer cars    Cab-end car

Length between drawbar centers to accommodate bridge limits: 50'-55'

"STEEL" CAR BLOCK

Capacity: 1000 t.    Length: 500'+

"Steel" car block (for ingots, slabs, plates, and other high weight density loads)

Cab-end car    2 trailer cars    Powered car    Tank    Powered car    Trailer car with auxiliary package    2 trailer cars    Cab-end car

BULK CAR BLOCK

Capacity: 1000 t.    Length: 600'+

(Bulk train employing 70 t. variant will use two more trailer cars per block; total length: 700')

Crossover locations

Cab-end car    5 trailer cars    Powered car    Tank    Powered car    4 trailer cars    Cab-end car

CONTAINER CAR BLOCK

Capacity: 50 20' containers    Length: 1200'+

## Economic Potential

Less than 2 billion dollars' worth of new gear can do all the hauling that railroads now find to do. Adding new trade and allowing for imperfect schedules, it would seem that the saturation point will be in the 3-to-5-billion-dollar range for equipment with a 10-year life. Once this fact is grasped and the new gear is under development, no more cars of present design need be or should be bought — present cars and engines can be worn out in makeshift integral trains while the new equipment is being made ready for market.

In terms of money, this means that by the time conversion is complete, the industry will have realized a large recovery of capital that can be invested in diversification. The railroad trade has too much capital in it now. The capital required for the change is actually negative. Some of us recall that the New York, Ontario & Western went diesel on rented engines when coal dealers put it on C.O.D. and General Motors wanted a showcase. So an outfit with no money converted first.

Equipment-ownership costs *per sold ton-miles* can be reduced by 95 per cent or more. Without modifying union contracts, labor cost can be reduced 80 per cent — and engine drivers will get $25 an hour or more. Track and accessory cost can be reduced almost 90 per cent. Transfer units can perform terminal work at 20 per cent to 50 per cent of the conventional costs. All this assuming, of course, that the new equipment is used at its best potential. A similar assumption on conventional equipment yields about one tenth the improvement.

Not all the savings need pass on to shippers. If we innovators find it necessary to inspire a new supplier, he will price his gear to get much of it himself. He probably will go direct to the customers — as aluminum salesmen went to can company customers — and trip-lease.

## Development Budget

The scheme has derived from shipper needs, and much has been learned about its commercial exploitation. Development budgets depend on what is included in "development." The money needed is not much. The industry's idea of development, however, is also pretty cheap. One carbuilder quibbled over the need for making a market study, and another rejected new designs with, "But our suppliers *have* patterns."

A reasonable budget for engineering and building a test/demonstrator set is a bit under 1 million dollars. Testing, demonstrating, promoting, and selling budget another 1 million; and 50 per cent contingency adds another. So there should be orders in the book after 3-million-dollar development money. It is still necessary to make the production-model designs and write the instruction book to tell railroads and shippers how best to use the equipment.

So a prospective entrepreneur needs 3 million dollars and would feel safer with 5 million. But the market is in billions, and the first units can be sold at extortionate markups — for specialized use, of course. Car blocks should sell (using cost-based prices with profits) in the $300,000 to $400,000 range and can be sold for quite some time at upwards of $700,000.

In the railroad trade, improvements have come from "outside." Even when an industrial conglomerate buys a carbuilder, it usually buys the help and

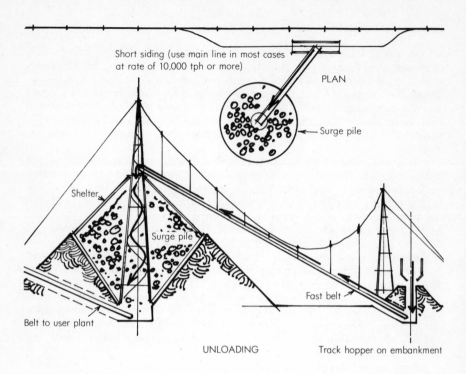

Short siding (use main line in most cases at rate of 10,000 tph or more)

PLAN

Surge pile

Shelter

Surge pile

Fast belt

Belt to user plant

UNLOADING

Track hopper on embankment

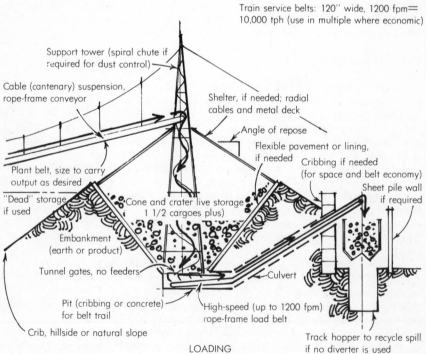

Train service belts: 120″ wide, 1200 fpm = 10,000 tph (use in multiple where economic)

Support tower (spiral chute if required for dust control)

Cable (cantenary) suspension, rope-frame conveyor

Shelter, if needed; radial cables and metal deck

Angle of repose

Flexible pavement or lining, if needed

Plant belt, size to carry output as desired

Cribbing if needed (for space and belt economy)

Sheet pile wall if required

"Dead" storage if used

Cone and crater live storage 1 1/2 cargoes plus)

Embankment (earth or product)

Tunnel gates, no feeders

Culvert

Pit (cribbing or concrete) for belt trail

High-speed (up to 1200 fpm) rope-frame load belt

Crib, hillside or natural slope

Track hopper to recycle spill if no diverter is used

LOADING

the attitudes. And there is a detectable reluctance to build a train. Doesn't everyone know that is the province of yardmasters? Two promising possibilities exist for a builder:

1. A user with application for several blocks will bury that first 1 million dollars and contingency in his own order. If he is that astute he will become a train vendor, and he can dominate the market as GM now dominates the engine business.

2. A foreigner — Japanese or German probably — who isn't afraid of the iron curtain between cars and engines will move in.

A third possibility is a North American builder of almost anything but railroad gear, but this isn't likely — few entrepreneur types in other businesses want anything to do with rails.

What do I care? It is getting monotonous telling shippers that the limitations of obsolete railroad tools force obsolete practices that hold costs so high that shippers have to use second-choice water or road transport. We need the new trains.

# APPENDIX B
# DEFINITIONS

This glossary is limited to terms that have special meanings in integral train technology. Planners of such systems are cautioned to use terms precisely — they can thereby avoid many long and frustrating discussions. Some of the terms have other meanings in other uses, and many disagreements are traceable to this cause.

**Bulk** — freight which moves, without packaging, in trainloads, for direct loading and unloading. The definition includes freight that is loaded or unloaded at several points in one trip.

**Capital offset** — a sum of money obtained by immediately liquidating an asset or commitment that is made unnecessary by an integral train system. In effect, the capital actually needed to install an integral train system is reduced, below what would be directly required to buy the system, by the amount of the capital offsets.

**Car** — rigorously, an assembly of railroad equipment extending from one separable coupler to the next, powered or not. Often used loosely to mean a carbody, which is defined as the equipment between successive points of articulation.

**Carbody** — see Car.

**Cargo** — the freight carried in one integral train on one trip — analogous to a vessel cargo as the train is analogous to a vessel.

**Cell** — part of a bulk storage terminal in which one commodity is stored separately from the contents of other cells.

**Compensatory** — in the regulatory sense, productive of revenue adequate to cover all direct or incremental costs and yield a contribution to "fixed" costs so that the operation need not be subsidized by money earned on other traffic. Sometimes arbitrarily defined as producing enough revenue to pay its own incremental cost and an administratively or politically determined contribution — semantically named a "fair share" — of common or fixed costs.

**Cone-and-crater bin** — an arrangement where bulk is piled in a conical pile within a ring embankment of fill or product, of which the volume of the crater plus the superimposed cone constitutes the live portion of the total storage capacity.

**Container** — a box or enclosure in which freight can be handled, usually without handling agencies having access to the freight itself. The definition is usually extended to include open-top units (sometimes called trays) and pallets equipped for handling in container systems.

**Container crane** — any device designed to handle containers by lifting and carrying them from above.

**Container transfer unit** — a specially designed or equipped truck capable of taking containers off of other trucks, platforms and cars and placing them on other trucks, platforms and cars by sliding them laterally (or longitudinally, though this variant will seldom arise).

**Cycle time** — total elapsed time of an integral train to complete a mission, including load, carry, unload, return, service, and delay times.

**Delay allowance** — time included in an estimated or projected cycle time for *unforeseen* delays from any source.

**E. T. A.** — estimated time of arrival — e.g., as supplied by a supervisor seeking to earn a time bonus or avoid a time penalty.

**Event cost** — the cost of performing a service or doing some work which is uniquely incurred whenever the service is performed or the work is done, whether recurring or not and not directly associated with time, miles or other external parameters — e.g., an inspection at an interchange.

**Fixed cost** — in context, a cost that does not vary directly with the choices available for a decision or operation being studied.

**F. T. D.** — money paid to members of a railroad crew who spend more than the contractual time from nominal arrival to release from duty, whether due to imposed delays or their own dilatory (unsupervised) movement.

**General cargo** — all freight that is not bulk, usually (in integral train systems) containerized. Usually includes carload-type goods such as salt or concentrates that move in "bulk" in containers for lack of whole-train volumes.

**Home** — a terminal at which railroad crews' wages start as defined in the pertinent labor agreement.

**IATI** — interest, amortization, taxes and insurance, sometimes called capital charge, comprising most but not all of ownership cost.

**Incremental costs** — in context, all costs incurred (net of savings) that are incurred if the operation being studied is carried out and which would not be incurred if it is not carried out. Alt.: in context, all costs incurred that vary among the choices actually available to a decision being studied.

**Initial maintenance** — of track, the maintenance required to make the track available, independently of traffic volume, numerically equal to total maintenance for track used at low volumes. Of other facilities, corresponding.

**Integral car block** — a fixed-consist set of equipment, self propelled or not, handled as a unit.

**Integral train** — a whole train, including its power, specialized or not, operated as a unit independently of general-purpose equipment and of other railroad subsystems.

**Integral train system** — a system consisting of an integral train (including spare elements) and the terminal and service accessories it needs to perform transportation.

**I. T. D.** — money paid to members of a railroad train crew who are called for duty but are not provided with employment within the contractual time, regardless of the amount of employment that may be offered for completion within 8 hours or any other period beginning at call time.

**Loading belt** — a terminal conveyor used to deliver bulk cargo to an integral train.

**Locomotive** — a separate piece of railroad equipment designed to produce tractive effort but not, itself, designed to carry payload.

**Mileage cost** — an element of an integral train budget that varies with distance traveled, in some manner capable of determination or estimate.

**Nondiscriminatory** — pragmatically, available to all similarly situated patrons on equivalent terms. The reverse — "discriminatory" — is sometimes used in an arbitrary manner to characterize operations that are objectionable to influential shippers or which fail to equalize nontransportation disabilities of unfortunately located or otherwise disadvantaged shippers.

**Nonreversing loop** — a track arrangement whereby a train can run in an endless pattern or path past a station or facility without reversing its direction of travel. See also Reversing loop.

**OH&P** — overhead and profit — for any enterprise a fund comprised of the total excess of revenues over incremental costs, from which overheads or fixed costs are first paid and whose residual is profit.

**Ownership cost** — total time-based cost of availability, including IATI, time-based maintenance and similar costs.

**Payload** — freight whose handling directly produces gross income.

**Power block** — a set of more or less permanently coupled integral train equipment containing motive power, whether also carrying payload or not. Used to define engine/fuel-car sets or engine/fuel-car/motored-payload-car sets.

**Relay** (verb) — to pass a railroad crew district boundary, changing crews without changing train consist or incurring avoidable delay; sometimes called a "main track connection" because the superficial characteristic is the use of a main, not a yard, track.

**Reversing loop** — a track arrangement on which a train can pass a station once and return whence it came without stopping.

**Rope belt** — a conveyor assembly in which the supporting frame is made of wire rope in place of the more common structural metal or timber bridge.

**Salvage** — (a) present: money obtained by selling an asset whose necessity to the operation is at an end, to produce a capital offset; or (b) prospective: money expected to be realized from actual or symbolic future sale of an asset whose amortization period or anticipated useful life has not yet ended.

**Supervised service** — a railroad service in which an attempt is made to monitor or control the movement of cars as distinguished from "conventional" service in which cars are moved in accordance with local application or interpretation of tariffs or generalized car service rules.

**Tariff** — a publication which lists the charges that common carriers make for services they offer, with conditions describing the services offered.

**Terminal** — in an integral train context, a facility for loading and unloading the train. Attention is directed to other definitions used for other uses.

**Time allowance** — time included in a projected schedule to perform certain work when the actual time required or even the need to perform the function at all is unknown, contingent or suspected of being avoidable; hence a time allowance may not be used, in whole or in part.

**Time bonus** — money recommended to be paid to a railroad beyond the basic rate as an incentive to completing missions faster than in the tariff-prescribed time.

**Time cost** — an integral train cost that runs in some relationship to elapsed time that can be estimated or determined.

**Time penalty** — a back-charge recommended to be made against a railroad for failing to complete a mission in the tariff-prescribed time.

**Train service belt** — a loading or an unloading belt.

**Transfer** (crew) — movement of a train for (usually) a short distance from one crew district to another by means of a yard or transfer crew within yard or terminal limits, local or interline.

**Transfer cell** — part of a bulk terminal used to receive a cargo rapidly for more leisurely transfer to other cells in the terminal or to receive cargo in leisurely fashion for rapid loading aboard an integral train; used to conserve train time.

**Trip cost** — an element of cost that occurs on each trip, generally independently of trip length or cargo carried.

**Tunnel gate** — a piece of hardware comprising a chute capable of being lifted or lowered to stop or regulate a flow of bulk material moving by gravity from a bin or cell onto a belt or fixed chute.

**Turn crew** — a railroad crew that makes a round trip from a crew dispatch point or crew terminal to a point intermediate between its origin and the far boundary of its district.

**Unit train system** — a system whereby more or less conventional cars are moved in a more or less supervised service with the capability and intention that part or all of the equipment be interchangeable with other general-purpose equipment, with or without control of the empty cars once a mission is completed.

**Unloading belt** — a conveyor in a bulk terminal used to move material directly from a track hopper to a storage or transfer cell.

**Yard crew** — a railroad train crew operating within contractual yard or switching limits and usually paid in terms of time and not in terms of miles.